CW00677676

Whiplash

THE CERVICAL SPINE IN MEDICO-LEGAL PRACTICE

Whiplash

THE CERVICAL SPINE IN MEDICO-LEGAL PRACTICE

J.W. Rodney Peyton

TD BSc MSc(Educ) MD FRCS(Eng,Ed & I) FRCP(Lond) PGDL

2004 MANTICORE BOOKS LIMITED

First published in Great Britain in 2004 by Manticore Books Limited
Silver Birches, Heronsgate, Rickmansworth, Herts. WD3 5DN

© J.W. Rodney Peyton, 2004

The right of J.W. Rodney Peyton to be identified as the author of this work has been asserted
by him in accordance with the Copyright, Designs and Patents Act 1988.

All rights reserved. No part of this book may be reproduced or transmitted in any form or by
any means, electronic or mechanical, including photocopying, recording, or any information
storage or retrieval system without the prior permission from the publisher.

While every attempt has been made to ensure that the information provided in this book is
correct at the time of printing, the publisher or its agents make no representation, express or
otherwise, with regard to the accuracy of the information contained herein and cannot accept
any legal responsibility or liability for any errors or omissions that may have been made or for
any loss or damage resulting from the use of the information.

Printed and bound in Great Britain by J.H.Haynes & Co. Ltd., Yeovil

British Library Cataloguing in Publication Data
A CIP record for this book is available from the British Library
ISBN 1 900887 09 6

Acknowledgement

I should like to acknowledge my colleagues who have assisted with this project: to Lynne Peyton for helping to edit the manuscript, to Christine Martin for typing the manuscript and to Lynn Johnston for providing several of the illustrations. Also to Richard Warman for helping to bring the book to fruition.

This book is dedicated to Lynne, Christopher, Jonathan and Timothy whose support and encouragement makes it all worthwhile.

Contents

Introduction   9

Chapter 1   Whiplash Injuries – A Modern Epidemic   11

Chapter 2   The Functional Anatomy of the Neck   15

Chapter 3   Mechanisms of Injury   25

Chapter 4   The Symptoms and Signs of Whiplash Injury   33

Chapter 5   Radiological Investigations   43

Chapter 6   Clinical Course and Management of Whiplash Injury   49

Chapter 7   Psychological Aspects of Whiplash Injury   53

Chapter 8   The Medico-legal Assessment and Report   61

Chapter 9   Giving Evidence in Court   71

Index   77

Introduction

Road traffic accidents represent a truly modern epidemic, causing over 3,000 deaths and more than 30,000 serious injuries worldwide every single day. Personal injury litigation has seen a concomitant rise, predominantly due to injuries to the spine and in particular to the cervical spine.

The basis of medico-legal practice is communication between medicine and the law about the physical and psychological consequences of these injuries. The starting point must therefore be a clear understanding of what each profession can contribute to the process and the specific role of the medical expert. An expert clinician is not necessarily an expert witness. Expertise as a medical witness requires skills which are not taught in medical school and which have to be developed through both training and exposure to good practice.

This book is written for lawyers—solicitors, barristers and judges, to assist them in understanding what they might reasonably expect of those they engage as experts in the field of whiplash injury. In order to gain maximum benefit from expert testimony, lawyers need to be familiar with the terminology relating to both physical and mental disease processes and to have an understanding of how the mechanisms involved actually cause injury. In addition they need an awareness of the influence of the various prognostic factors.

It is also written as an aid to doctors providing expert reports and testimony, who need to fully comprehend that the duty of the expert witness is to assist the Court, ensuring that physical and mental injuries are fully acknowledged but not unfairly exaggerated. The style and nature of the presentation of evidence is therefore vitally important. The value of any claim is directly proportional to the skill with which the doctor carries out this task, both in the clarity and logic of the written medico-legal report and its prognosis and when necessary, in the clear presentation of findings and analysis from the witness box.

Medico-legal practice differs from normal clinical practice in that the history and mechanism of injury rather than clinical management assumes greater importance. The consistency of the findings on examination with the mechanism of injury and the clinical signs requires a detailed analysis, culminating in an intelligent 'guestimate' of the likely long-term prognosis based on the best evidence available. Medical experts must also be prepared to contemplate any different evidence or scenarios presented to them and render a considered and logical response. Unfortunately some patients in a medico-legal context may be 'economical with the truth' and it is the duty of the medical expert to be totally independent and to highlight inconsistencies, regardless of which side is instructing them.

This book will therefore be essential for general practitioners, who may occasionally be called upon to write reports and to give evidence, particularly in the lower courts. The material presented will give them firm ground for basing their opinions and a clear structure for the production of reports. In particular, guidance is given in those fields which clinicians do not normally address in any detail, such as the mechanism of injury and the importance of showing causation, not only describing the physical findings but commenting on the consistency of those findings with the clinical situation and the emotional sequelae. It will be equally invaluable to hospital staff embarking on the medico-legal aspects of their career, in specialities such as accident and emergency, general and orthopaedic surgery, or rheumatology. For those who are already expert witnesses it will enhance their ability to communicate effectively within the legal process.

1

Whiplash Injuries – A Modern Epidemic

INTRODUCTION

The existence of whiplash injury following a road traffic accident has been the subject of much controversy. There are those who would doubt its very existence and others who feel that even if it does exist, its prevalence is much exaggerated due to the potential for litigation.

Controversy also arises because the term 'whiplash' is a description of a mechanism of injury rather than a medical diagnosis. It is a term applied to a collection of symptoms caused by soft tissue injuries to the musculo-ligamentous tissues, joints, discs, spinal cord and nerve roots of the cervical spine, as the result of flexion and/or extension movements, which may be coupled with elements of sheer and rotation. Occasionally there may be bony damage, for instance a ligamentous avulsion (tearing), a compression fracture to the vertebral body or a dislocation possibly associated with a fracture of the facetal joints, although this is very unusual.

Whiplash is most commonly associated with road traffic accidents. In the majority of cases there is a rear end collision although symptoms may arise after impact from any angle. Similar damage may sometimes be caused by a sports injury or a fall.

HISTORICAL PERSPECTIVE

The first recorded use of the term *whiplash* was by Dr Harold Crowe at a conference in San Francisco in 1928. He was actually describing the motion of the head on the shoulders after sudden impact from a road traffic accident but the term whiplash quickly came into common usage in the medical and legal professions as well as by lay people, to describe the *effects* of the trauma, not only on the neck but on occasions on other areas of the spine. Road traffic accidents and hence the incidence of these injuries have now reached truly epidemic proportions as it is estimated that at least one in every 200 of the population will be involved in a road traffic accident in any one year.

IMPACT OF CAR DESIGN AND SAFETY FEATURES

Modern design and safety features in cars have had a considerable effect on the prevalence of whiplash. The main cause of the injury is the differential effect of transmission of force to the trunk and the head. The amount of force available in the first instance depends on the momentum of impact and whether or not that force is dissipated by the victim's vehicle, either by forward motion or by deformability of the bodywork–crumple zones. Proper positioning of an appropriate headrest should in theory stop the head moving backwards. However, most of the time there is a space between the back of the head and the headrest and indeed some drivers are inclined to sit with their head well forward. Therefore, on impact, the head is jerked back into the headrest which can lead to contusion in the brain. Also, many headrests are not properly adjusted and the most common position is to be fully retracted. In many impacts it has been shown that the body actually rises from the seat, particularly on impacts from behind. This sudden elevation, combined with a low headrest, allows the head to flip backwards over the top of the headrest which therefore acts as a fulcrum, compounding the neck extension (figure 1). On the contrary, some modern seats have been designed to be less rigid with the seat back tending to give way on impact thereby decreasing the transmitted force as the head comes to an abrupt halt.

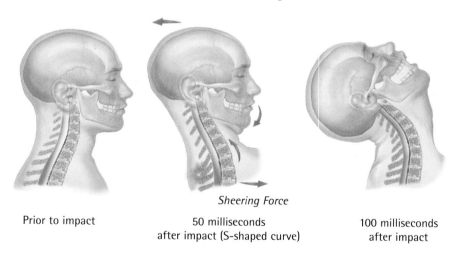

Sheering Force

Prior to impact

50 milliseconds
after impact (S-shaped curve)

100 milliseconds
after impact

Fig.1 Whiplash - mechanics of motion after impact

Although undoubtedly saving many lives as well as markedly diminishing the amount of facial and chest trauma, seatbelt legislation in the UK has been shown to increase the likelihood of neck injury. The problems are twofold. The first is that the cross portion of the belt restricts the forward motion of the trunk and the unrestrained head therefore continues to rotate forward into flexion until the chin strikes the chest. There also may be some forward movement and sheering between the vertebrae, especially in the lower cervical region near the more fixed point of the thoracic spine (see figure 1). Secondly, the cross belt tends to rotate the trunk when it is thrown forward, as it differentially fixes one shoulder. The head starts to move forward but the rotation of the shoulders causes a twisting of the neck.

Theoretically, the deployment of the airbag in a frontal collision may prevent at least some of the forward motion of the head on the trunk. It may also diminish some of the rotation and therefore may prove to lessen the effects. However, this is not yet proven, and in any case the airbag is not normally deployed in a rear end collision.

MEDICO-LEGAL PERSPECTIVES

The basis of medico-legal practice in relation to whiplash must be set in the context of the accident, the victim, the medical consequences and the law.

There would perhaps be less antagonism if the more accurate term 'acute neck strain' was utilised. The author has personal experience of being questioned in court by senior counsel as to whether or not an injury could be termed whiplash if the impact was frontal, since the initial coining of the term by Crowe only referred to rear end impacts!

The basic questions that need to be addressed are:

1 Are the symptoms and signs consistent?

2 Are there any pre-existing overt or covert problems in the claimant that may have an effect on the nature of the injury and its long-term consequences?

3 What is the long-term outlook for recovery?

4 What is the likelihood of such symptoms developing anyway without the intervention of the accident?

5 What is the influence of the level of symptoms?

6 On the balance of probabilities, what degree of the present and any possible future loss of amenity is directly due to the incident in question?

The answers to all of these questions require a fundamental understanding of the mechanism and nature of the injury sustained, the relevance of the findings on clinical examination and the likely impact of those factors that influence the long-term outlook. This is especially important because neck pain is a common complaint with the frequency increasing with age and in certain occupations. It has been shown in some studies using Magnetic Resonance Imaging (MRI) that over 50% of patients over fifty years of age already display degenerative changes in the cervical spine, but may be totally asymptomatic.

The term 'whiplash' has different connotations for the medical and legal professions and the interrelationships between all the factors involved are complex, particularly if litigation is protracted. Professionals involved in the process need to be aware of the impact of a road traffic accident and the consequent legal process on the claimant's physical and mental well-being.

CHAPTER HIGHLIGHTS

1 Whiplash is the term used to describe a collection of symptoms caused by a soft tissue injury to the neck.

2 Whiplash injuries are most commonly caused by road traffic accidents.

3 In medico-legal practice it is essential to have a thorough history and assessment and to set the injury in the context of the accident itself, the claimant's particular medical, occupational and social circumstances and the likely future implications.

2

The Functional Anatomy of the Neck

INTRODUCTION

In order to comprehend the physical consequences of a whiplash injury it is first necessary to understand the anatomy of the neck and then to be familiar with the range of normal movements. The anatomy of the neck has developed as a compromise of rigidity–to protect the spinal cord, and flexibility–to allow movements of the head. As in any compromise there are inevitable weaknesses and these are highlighted when the neck is subjected to abnormal stress such as during a road traffic accident.

NORMAL ANATOMY

The neck compromises the following components:

1 Vertebrae

2 Facetal joints

3 Intervertebral discs

4 Spinal nerves

5 Spinal cord

6 Ligaments

7 Other soft tissues

The Vertebrae

The cervical spine consists of seven vertebrae which connect the base of the skull to the trunk. Under normal circumstances these are very mobile with the first cervical vertebra (the *atlas*) connecting to the base of the skull and the seventh cervical vertebra ('C7') articulating with the first thoracic vertebra.

The neck forms a natural curve, concave posteriorly. The structure of a vertebra is as seen in figure 2. Anteriorly is the main mass of bone termed the body of the vertebra. Posteriorly is an arch, in the centre of which runs the spinal or vertebral canal. At the apex of this arch is the thickened spinous

Transverse plane view of the neck

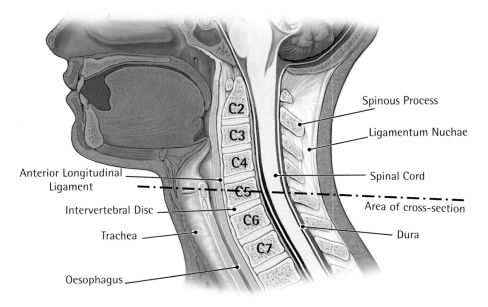

Sagittal view through the neck at C5

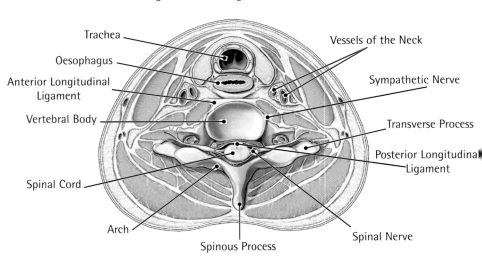

Fig. 2 Normal anatomy of the neck, transverse plane and sagittal views

process. The most prominent of these is at C7 at the base of the neck and forming an obvious landmark which can be easily examined. This is known as the *vertebra prominens*. On either side at the junction between the arches and the body of the vertebra is a lateral mass called the *transverse process*.

The first two cervical vertebrae are slightly different from the rest. The first vertebra, the *atlas*, articulates with the base of the skull. It is in the shape of a ring with the main portion of the body being detached and fused with the body of the second cervical vertebra ('C2' the *axis*), which therefore appears to protrude into the ring of the first vertebra as a peg known as the *odontoid peg* or *dens* (figure 3).

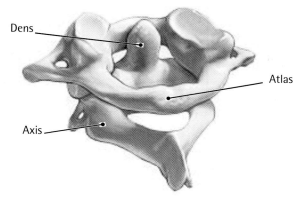

Fig. 3 The Atlas and Axis

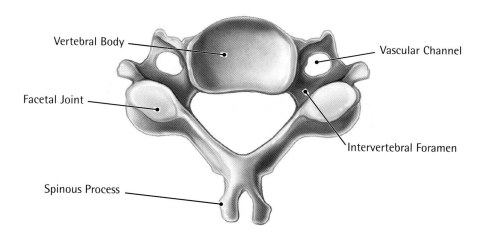

Fig. 4 A typical Cervical Vertibra

17

Facetal Joints

On each of the lateral masses there are two joints, one above and one below to articulate with the similar joints of the vertebrae above and below. These are the *facetal* or *zygopophyseal* joints (see figure 5). They have a synovial lining and a surrounding fibrous capsule to allow movement. The superior joint normally faces backwards and the lower joint forwards although they are more flattened at the level of C2 in order to allow greater movement at this level. These joints contain a lot of pain fibres which are stimulated when the joint is under tension, for instance when it is inflamed or a fold of synovium is trapped following trauma. Such a fold may be freed by manipulation.

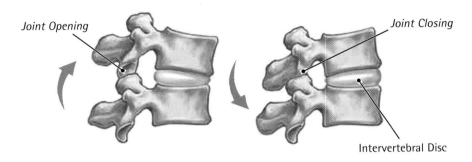

Fig. 5 The Facetal Joint at C4

Intervertebral Discs

Between each of the bodies there is an intervertebral disc which allows some movement in all planes and acts as a shock absorber. Under normal circumstances the upright posture causes some compression of all discs throughout the spine and in an adult this may mean between 1 and 2cm difference in height between getting out of bed in the morning and spending a number of hours in the erect position.

The centre of the disc is of gelatinous material, the *nucleus pulposus*, which is held in place by a surrounding coat of fibrocartilaginous tissue firmly attached to the adjacent vertebral bodies. This is very strong and is known as the *annulus fibrosus*. It can tolerate forces such as compression, bending and twisting but it does deteriorate with age. However, since there are no nerves in the area of the disc, no pain is felt until there has been significant damage to the annulus fibrosus. Pain can therefore arise from the annulus fibrosus itself or, if it bulges backwards and compresses the nerve roots, from the spinal cord. The most common sites of such deterioration are at the level of C5/6 and C6/7.

Spinal Nerves

Just anterior to the interfacetal joints is a gap termed the *intervertebral foramen* (see figures 2 and 4) through which the nerve roots exit the spinal canal. Among other things these nerves supply motor function to the muscles from the brain and transmit sensory function from the periphery back to the brain. Any narrowing of this foramen may cause signs and symptoms in the territory of the nerve. Initially the problems may be of sensory origin such as pain and tingling but later may also involve the motor function, giving rise to some weakness. Such a narrowing may be caused by dislocation of the interfacetal joints allowing one to slip forward on the other, by swelling of the joints caused by soft tissue inflammation around the joint, or by arthritic change narrowing the foramina. If the disc between the main intervertebral bodies bulges posteriorly in this region, compression of the nerve root may be caused.

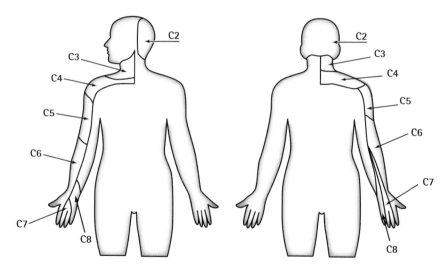

Fig 6. 2nd to 8th Dermatome location

There are eight cervical nerves. The first emerges above the atlas, between it and the skull and this is the only root which does not carry sensation from the skin. The next seven nerves also arise above the appropriate vertebra but the eighth arises below the seventh vertebra, between it and the first thoracic vertebra. Each one of the second to the eighth nerve roots supply particular regions of the skin's surface known as dermatomes and these are illustrated in figure 6. Any disturbance of these nerve roots may give rise to abnormal sensation in their distribution. Therefore, problems at the level of C2 may give

19

rise to pain in the back of the head causing a sensation of posterior headache. Disturbance of C3 may cause pain to the angle of the jaw and around the ear. C4 involves the sides and base of the neck and C5 down the anterior aspect of the arm to an area just above the elbow. It does not supply the hand. C6 involves the lateral or outer aspect of the arm to the thumb, C7 to the index and middle fingers and C8 to the ring and fifth fingers. Without severe disruption to the nerves it is unusual to find any weakness of muscle although there may appear to be a weakness as patients may avoid fully using the power of the muscle because movement is painful.

Spinal Cord

The spinal cord is found within the spinal canal, which is the area behind the body of the vertebrae and the discs surrounded by the bony arch. The spinal cord runs from the brain to the lower thoracic and upper lumbar regions. It is rarely damaged in the cervical region since it only occupies up to half of the available space. However, if this space becomes narrowed, either due to severe arthritic change or an acute posterior protrusion of a disc, the cord may be compressed. This may cause paradoxical problems in the elderly, whereby the more peripheral nerve roots are relatively spared but rather the central fibres in the cord are damaged. This area of the cord supplies the legs, and neck injuries in the elderly may result in more symptoms related to the lower limbs than the upper limbs—a classic anatomical trap for the unwary examiner.

Closely applied to the inner aspect of the vertebral canal is the dura with the arachnoid layer being applied between the dura and the cord. In this layer circulates the protective cerebro-spinal fluid.

The Ligaments

The anterior longitudinal ligament runs down the front of the vertebral column. It is firmly attached to the anterior portions of the discs and it is not visible on an ordinary x-ray. It may become visible if it becomes calcified as a consequence of age or following trauma. Similarly, the posterior longitudinal ligament runs down the posterior surface of the body on the vertebrae.

The *ligamentum flavum* (yellow ligament) runs laterally between the arches of the vertebrae and blends with the capsule of each interfacetal joint. Posteriorly is the strong *ligamentum nuchae* in the cervical region, joining each of the spinus processes and, along with the main muscles of the neck, this helps to hold the head erect. There is also a strong ligament joining the lateral transverse processes called the *intra-transverse ligament*.

Other Soft Tissues

The main muscles surrounding the neck may go into spasm if the nerves have been damaged or when they themselves become partially torn in an accident. The two main muscles at the sides of the neck are called the *sternocleidomastoid muscles*. Contraction of one of these would turn the head to the opposite side and any attempt to bring the head back to the neutral position may cause pain if the muscle is damaged. The main muscle at the back of the neck spreading across the shoulders and down into the thoracic area is the *trapezius* which, following a whiplash injury, may feel tight due to spasm with pain and tenderness radiating down the sides of the neck, across the shoulders and down between the shoulder blades.

Deep to the trapezius muscle is another muscle which frequently goes into spasm following whiplash injury. It is the *elevator scapula* which is a common trigger point for pain. Other muscles in the same general area are the *semispinatus capitus* which is a strong muscle running from the transverse processes of the lower cervical and upper thoracic vertebrae to the back of the shoulder. Other small 'capitus' muscles attach C1 and C2 to the base of the skull.

The scalene muscles connect the spine to the ribs. *Scalenus anterior* runs between the processes of C4 to C6 and the first rib with *scalenus medius* arising from C2 to C7 and attaching to the first rib. The brachial plexus of nerves is closely applied to these muscles and compression due to spasm of the muscle may cause pain down the arm.

Closely applied to the front of the vertebrae is the oesophagus. It starts at the level of the larynx, around C3 or C4. Any swelling in the area of the anterior longitudinal ligament may therefore compress this organ giving rise to a feeling of difficulty in swallowing (see figure 2). Anterior to the oesophagus is the trachea, leading to the lungs.

On either side of these organs are the main blood vessels supplying the head. It is most unusual for these to be damaged in a whiplash scenario but occasionally the seatbelt can dig into the side of the neck, damaging in particular the carotid artery.

DYNAMICS OF THE NECK

In personal injury litigation following a road traffic accident, the neck is the area most commonly involved. Therefore, a working knowledge of the function and the anatomy of the cervical spine is vital to all those involved in the legal process, in order to make sense of any symptom complex as well as to understand the results of any tests that are performed, particularly if these appear to suggest there may be a functional overlay or evidence of malingering.

When describing the movements of the neck it is assumed that there is an erect posture facing forward. The four main movements are:

1 Flexion
2 Extension
3 Rotation
4 Lateral flexion

Flexion is the action of placing the chin down on the chest while extension is the opposite movement whereby the head is tilted backwards and has been described as 'putting the nose into the air'. Rotation is keeping the head level and turning from side to side to look over the corresponding shoulder. Lateral flexion is facing forward and putting the head so that the ear approaches the corresponding shoulder.

The range of flexion and extension is such that 50% occurs at the *atlanto occipital joint* between the base of the skull and C1. Most of the rest of these movements occur at the levels of C1/2 and C5/6.

It is important to note that, in general terms, loss of movements of the neck are not due to spasm but are more commonly due to a voluntary act for example when the patient is unwilling to move the neck fully because of pain. However, there is a fine line between this and a deliberate attempt to mislead the examiner. The movements should be tried several times and, providing there is some movement, consistency of findings over a number of examinations would suggest a genuine difficulty.

Movements of the neck involve a combination of flexion, extension, rotation and lateral flexion. The 'normal' range will vary depending on age and body habitus, for instance a long thin neck may have a greater range of movement than a short bull neck. However, in the normal young adult, the following minimal movements would be expected (see figure 7).

By the age of forty these ranges begin to decrease particularly around the levels of C5 to C7 and the normal seventy year-old will only display approximately

 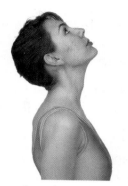

Forward flexion 60 degrees   Extension 80 degrees

Rotation to either side 70 degrees

Lateral flexion to either side 60 degrees

Fig. 7 Illustrations of normal Flexion, Extension, Rotation and Lateral flexion

23

two-thirds of these values. As disc space narrows due to degenerative change, the range of movement decreases. This leads to stress in the joints giving rise to pain which in turn further reduces the range. Pressure around the nerves can cause a sharp pain on turning the head from side to side or on looking up and down. This pain may be referred to other areas such as the back of the head, around the ear and jaw or down the arms and after on prolonged standing, there may be a feeling of weakness in the muscles around the neck. These ranges can only be taken as a guide. Any congenital abnormality such as fusion of two or more vertebrae will diminish the mobility to a varying extent. Such loss of mobility may render the neck more liable to give rise to symptoms after an accident. In a patient with a short fat neck, movements may be reduced by up to one third.

ASSESSMENT

On examination in these cases, the two most important findings are the level of restriction in the movement of the neck and the consistency with which the restriction is demonstrated. This should be assessed through a formal examination of the full range of neck movements and also by observation of the claimant at all times throughout the interview. The way the patient walks into the room and the ease with which they move and put on clothing and move during conversation, tie and untie shoes, are all important indicators of the degree of disability.

CHAPTER HIGHLIGHTS

1 Road traffic accidents commonly cause symptoms in the neck because the trauma exposes the inherent and anatomical weakness of the cervical spine.

2 In the context of medico-legal assessment it is essential to understand the basic anatomy and range of normal movements of the neck. These will vary with age and circumstances, including congenital abnormalities, underlying disease processes and any previous trauma.

3 Formal examination and careful ongoing observation of neck movements throughout the interview is fundamental to the assessment process.

3

Mechanisms of Injury

INTRODUCTION

The nature and severity of injury to drivers and passengers involved in road traffic accidents will depend on a number of factors. These include the speed of the vehicle and the force of the impact, the direction of impact, the nature of the neck movements of individual passengers, and whether individuals collide with fixed objects or each other. This chapter considers these influences and the range and nature of possible neck movements during collision.

INFLUENCE OF SPEED

The momentum caused by the impact depends on the relative weights and speeds of the two vehicles, which therefore influences the potential for energy transferred. Obviously the harder the impact, the more energy is liable to transfer to both the vehicle and its occupants and hence the greater the damage that might occur. The actual force transmitted to the occupants depends in the first incidence on what happens to the vehicle. If the vehicle starts to move forward and/or crumples, the vehicle itself absorbs some of the force leaving less to be transmitted to the occupants. If however, the vehicle then stops quickly, for instance after hitting another object, there is a greater impact of the force on the body. The same is true if the occupants, having been pushed forward are suddenly stopped by the seatbelts.

Whiplash injuries can occur with impact speeds of as little as 5 miles per hour. Estimated forces at this level are as much as five times gravity. The force of 20 miles per hour has been measured at around twelve times gravity following a rear impact on a stationery vehicle. However, even at low speeds the consequences for passengers are significant and although the acceleration force in the car itself may be around five times gravity, the momentum of the head on the body can reach a force of around twelve times gravity during the extension phase.

The tension in the muscles of the neck at the time of impact is particularly important in low speed impacts. This may well explain why rear end impacts have the greatest effect since at that time the occupants of the car may not be aware of the impending collision. Those involved in frontal impacts however have time to brace both their neck and their bodies giving at least some protective effect. Similarly, a driver who sees the likelihood of impact in his rear view mirror may have time to brace his neck and also his arms against the steering wheel whereas the passengers may not have such a warning. This may indeed protect the driver's neck, however the bracing of his arms against the steering wheel may lead to pain in the posterior aspect of the upper arms over the area of the triceps and in the inner forearm.

This raises issues as to how to explain the lack of reported symptoms after bumper car rides in a fairground where the intent is obviously to hit the car in front. It is suggested that the lack of injury is due to the fact that the cars travel at low speeds and at the time of impact in a bumper car, the occupants are prepared and therefore have time to put the muscles in the neck under tension. At low velocity this has the effect of markedly diminishing any relative movement between the head and the torso through the neck and therefore soft tissue damage does not occur. However, all such rides carry warnings that those with neck and back problems should not participate. In a rear end car collision, the occupants are not generally braced for the impact and therefore the peak acceleration movements that ensue do cause disruption to the soft tissue of the neck.

In the absence of local trauma directly to the neck region, the root cause of the whiplash injury is the differential movement between the head and the trunk. This is compounded by the elastic recoil of the discs, the ligaments and the muscles but the differential momentum of the head and body is the main causative factor and this increases with speed.

It is therefore obvious that if the head and trunk moved as one piece there would be much less likelihood of injury. Under normal circumstances in a vehicle, the position of the driver and passengers relative to the back of the seat and any headrest can actually contribute to injury as will be discussed later.

DIRECTION OF IMPACT

In road traffic accidents, the most common impact is from the rear although it may occur anywhere in the 360 degrees surrounding the vehicle. The direction of force applied to the neck varies with the nature and direction of the impact. Many attempts have been made to show this using cine-radiography, however it is very difficult to extrapolate movements noted in a small number of cases under test conditions to the majority of victims in real accidents. However, some features do become obvious. In frontal impacts, the body moves forward away from the headrest. There is some recoil but the impact between the headrest and the back of the head is much less than it would be in a similar posterior impact. Symptoms are therefore more significant when hit from behind. Injuries can occur throughout the cervical spine, but the major fixed points are just below the skull at the level of C1 and C2 and at the base of the neck. C7 is particularly tightly applied to the first thoracic vertebra and therefore the major movement against a fixed point occurs at the junctions between C5/6 and C6/7.

Impact is not limited to a horizontal plane since the vehicle may be lifted upwards or even rolled. The torso is held in a restrained position and the head is free to move in any direction with resultant forces applied to the neck.

NATURE OF NECK MOVEMENTS

Separating out the forces give rise to the following 'pure' movements:

Flexion and Extension

Within the normal range of movement the neck can flex fully forward until the chin touches the chest. In an accident the chin may strike the chest with sufficient force as to cause bruising. Such flexion may also be accompanied by a distraction (separation) with the head literally pulling away from the trunk, over stretching the muscles and ligaments of the back of the neck as well as the interfacetal joints.

On impact, extension on the other hand may far exceed the normal range of 70 degrees particularly if there is no headrest. Indeed as noted earlier, a low headrest may simply act as a fulcrum with the head going back over the top putting even further stretch on the anterior portions of the neck and compression of the posterior elements. This may lead to stretching in the area of the discs and particularly the anterior longitudinal ligament and compression of the spinus processes and of the interfacetal joints. In a rear end shunt it has been postulated that the first movement is that the trunk is pushed forward and, since the head is not against the headrest, it, by inertia, first hyper-extends to the extent that it can. The neck then recoils and flexes on the trunk to its limit of the chin touching the chest followed by lesser recoils into extension and flexion until motion ceases. Less force may be applied if the back of the seat breaks or if it comes out of its mountings and so lessens the resultant forces applied to the body.

In a true rear end shunt there may also be a sheering movement as the lower vertebra glides forward against the upper. This will tend to be limited by the ligaments and may distract or open up the interfacetal joints. On the other hand a head on collision will sheer in the other direction causing compression of the interfacetal joints. This movement of the joints may be one of the main pathways of chronic pain.

Rotation

These movements may be compounded by an element of rotation if the victim is not facing directly forwards at the time of the impact. This rotational element may also lead to increased strain on the ligaments and joints. It has also been shown that in rear end impacts, the torso may be forced upwards relative to the head, transmitting an upward force through the cervical spine. This area normally has a curve, concave posteriorly. When an upward force is applied, cine-radiographs have shown that the lower cervical vertebrae unfold first, followed progressively by the rest of the cervical spine. The head is also pushed upwards elongating the neck and adding to the distraction.

Rotation movement of the neck or the torso may be present initially because the victim is looking to one side and not straight ahead. Rotational forces may also be caused when the torso is pushed forward and held on one side, for instance by the cross belt holding one shoulder and allowing the other to come forward and therefore rotate. Other scenarios include when the driver has one hand on the steering wheel relatively fixing that shoulder or in the case of a passenger, one hand against the dashboard or against the back of the seat in front. Rotational movement has least effect on a central passenger in the back seat because this passenger is wearing only a lap belt. The rotational element from the belt will therefore be missing, however the body can be thrown forward over the belt and as a result cause greater extension and distraction.

Lateral Flexion

The other pure movements of the neck are those of lateral flexion while the normal range in a young adult is 50 to 60 degrees, lateral flexion may occur until it is stopped by the side of the head striking the shoulder which could easily be 110 degrees. This causes considerable over-flexion on one side and over-distraction on the other, along with the usual recoil to the other side in a manner similar to the initial description of flexion and extension.

The forces involved are therefore a combination of forward flexion, posterior extension, rotation, lateral flexion, sheer, compression and distraction. Theoretical discussions about which comes first are largely irrelevant.

As noted above, all of these movements are compounded by the recoil of the neck. The effects can be further exacerbated in situations where there is a double impact either because of the nature of the accident, for instance being shunted into the vehicle in front, or if the driver or passenger's head hits another object within the car such as a steering wheel, the windscreen, the roof, the headrest or the seat in front.

The degree to which the available movements occur depends on the forces applied. This in turn is dependent on the speed of impact, the angle of impact, as well as whether or not the brakes were applied. The subsequent deformation of the vehicle (which is its ability to absorb forces which are therefore not transmitted to the body), the elasticity of the seats, the relative position of any headrest, the weight of the body and the shape of the neck, are all factors which contribute to the severity of injury.

INFLUENCE OF THE HEADREST

Headrests are designed to prevent hyper-extension of the neck and are now standard in all automobiles. While they are essential to prevent severe neck injuries caused by the head whipping backwards, they do of themselves contribute to some injuries, particularly if not properly fitted and used. In normal driving situations it is unusual for the back of the head to be in contact with the headrest, and indeed many drivers sit forward with their upper back not resting on the seat. On impact from behind therefore the pelvis and lower back are held by the lap belt in close proximity to the seat. The shoulders initially move backwards hitting the seat, the back of the skull strikes the headrest if it is properly positioned and this is equivalent to a blow on the back of the head. The headrest may therefore protect against hyperextension if it is properly positioned but, since it was not initially closely applied to the skull, may actually cause direct trauma to the head resulting in cerebral contusion. Another feature of a rigid headrest is that these may cause facial injuries to backseat passengers particularly in smaller cars where the distance between front and rear seats is limited.

AIRBAGS

In theory, airbags should give protection by absorbing some of the forward movement on the trunk and the head thereby lessening the recoil. However, the initial forward and backward movement along with hyperextension of the neck would not be affected and it is not surprising that to date airbags have not been seen to reduce the incidence of cervical spine damage.

EFFECTS ON TISSUES

Impacts in road traffic accidents do have effects on all the soft tissues of the neck (see figure 2). Muscles tend to tear with some local bleeding or at least have an inflammatory reaction with a tendency to swell which explains the delay in onset of problems. Smaller ligaments in the discs may be damaged with the impact, including the anterior longitudinal ligament. However as the posterior longitudinal ligament is so strong, if it was ruptured it is most likely the patient would have died.

Small areas of bruising may occur in front of the cervical spine causing swelling known as a *pre-vertebral haematoma*. This swelling pushes against the back of the throat involving the recurrent laryngeal nerve and can give rise to a sore throat and some hoarseness. Mechanical pressure on the oesophagus can cause difficulty in swallowing. Occasionally damage to the sympathetic nerves in this region can give rise to a loss of the sympathetic tone involving one or other eye in which case the pupil would dilate.

Some small fractures especially of the pedicals and laminae may occur. These are very difficult to see on x-ray but may be suspected when soft tissue swelling is noted. Coned views or a CT Scan may then be indicated. In younger people with supple tissues, larger movements can occur without ripping tissues because of the larger range in movement and greater elasticity.

It has been demonstrated that in those with pre-existing degenerative changes, whether or not they were previously symptomatic, the effect of the trauma is usually more significant, giving rise to a greater likelihood of long-term symptoms. There is however no evidence whatsoever that degenerative changes are actually caused by accidents, therefore degenerative changes noted on the x-ray perhaps a year or more after the accident cannot be attributed to the incident although they may have significance in long-term symptomatology that will be discussed in the next chapter.

TAKING A HISTORY

For litigation purposes it is important that a clear and coherent history is taken and that careful attentions is paid to certain elements in the mechanisms of injury. It is essential to elicit answers to the following:

1 A brief description of the accident.

2 Was the car moving or stationary and if stationary was the brake on?

3 What was the direction of impact and the approximate speed?

4 Did the car have headrests, were these properly adjusted and were all of the

5 occupants wearing seatbelts?

6 Did the occupants anticipate the collision and have time to brace?

7 What happened after impact?

8 Were the occupants thrown forward, did they hit the roof or the back of their head on the headrest?

9 Was the airbag deployed?

10 Was it a single, double or multiple impact?

11 Was the car thrown upwards?

12 Did it roll?

13 Did any of the occupants have any bruising on the chest or tenderness in the back of the head?

14 Are the claimants aware of any pre-existing problems with their neck or back?

CHAPTER HIGHLIGHTS

1 Injuries to the neck are consequent upon extremes of movement of the neck or the shoulders caused by sudden impact, even at low speeds.

2 The extent of damage is also determined by the direction of impact, the presence of any safety features and the actual nature of neck movements.

3 Consequences for all of the individuals in a car will be different and careful histories are needed for each claimant.

The Symptoms and Signs of Whiplash Injury

INTRODUCTION

The symptoms of whiplash injury are varied as is the timing of their onset. It is not unusual for all the passengers in a vehicle to report different levels of symptoms. One may have no initial complaints whilst another may report severe pain in their neck and shoulders. This chapter considers the range of presentations which may occur with whiplash injuries and where possible identifies common features.

EARLY SYMPTOMS

For the majority it is difficult to generalise. Some degree of neck pain develops at the time or during the next 24 to 48 hours. Thereafter, the level of symptoms tends to increase, particularly over the first week. Indeed, it is not uncommon for the victim to continue working for several days before seeing their general practitioner (GP) and then going off work. Pain may remain constant and severe for perhaps two to eight weeks before easing and becoming intermittent. Symptoms in the majority of victims would be expected to settle in three to six months, however a significant proportion, perhaps one in 4 will still have symptoms of varying degrees after one year. Around 10% of all accident victims will have more long-term problems of a physical nature. Psychological trauma following road traffic accidents is more frequent than previously supposed and will be discussed further in chapter 7.

The following are the main symptoms following a whiplash injury.

Head Injury

Many victims report being stunned or dazed immediately after the accident and this phase may be associated with dizziness and nausea. Significant numbers report sitting in the car 'just wondering what happened' and taking a while to get their thoughts together. This may be a natural reaction of shock following the sudden and perhaps unexpected incident but two other mechanisms may also come into play.

The first is the occurrence of direct trauma or blow to the head. The head may have struck the headrest to the rear or been thrown forward hitting the steering wheel, window or sun visor. On occasions the body may have been pushed upwards hitting the roof, or laterally, hitting the door or window. All of these impacts could lead to direct cerebral contusion. The second mechanism is that the cervical spine may have been pushed upwards into the base of the skull, having the potential to jar the brain from below.

There are therefore adequate explanations for a degree of head injury following an accident which may give rise to headaches, nausea and dizziness for several days. Occasionally there may be complaints of a disturbance of vision. This is well-accepted clinically although the exact mechanisms are not proven.

Effects of Over Breathing

Also in the initial phase, the victim may become upset and over breathe. The drop in carbon dioxide levels caused by this may give feelings of tingling in the lips, the hands and the feet which may be recorded on an early admission to hospital. This type of tingling known as *paraesthesia* clears fairly quickly when the initial fright of the incident subsides. It may however be exacerbated by fear especially in situations where victims have had to be extracted from a vehicle, strapped onto a spinal board, given oxygen and transported, being monitored in an ambulance.

Headache

The most commonly reported initial complaints and findings are pain and stiffness in the back of the neck, perhaps radiating out towards the shoulders, and associated with a posterior headache. On examination there may be tenderness down the sides of the neck, across the shoulders and into the area between the shoulder blades, sometimes accompanied by muscle spasm and also associated with some restriction in movement. In more severe cases, pain can radiate to the hands. The headache, which is usually posterior in nature, can be very intense, increased by any movement of the head or by activities such as coughing. When posterior headaches are severe they can radiate right across the top of the head to the area behind the eyes and a number of victims report the character of the headache changing over the first few days from a generalised pain, to being more specifically posterior or anterior (frontal). It is felt that the continuing posterior headaches are related to referred pain of the nerves at the C2, C3 level which gives sensory input from this area. At the same time pain may also radiate out from this area of the neck to the back of the jaw at the area around the ears. It may be constant to begin with but usually starts to ease after three to four weeks, with the pains becoming less frequent over the space of six to nine months although very occasionally lasting beyond this. Prolonged frontal headache, on the other hand, is more usually related to tension and the claimant may well describe how the pain increases when they are tense, for instance when driving a car.

Neck and Shoulder Pain

Commonly the claimant complains of feeling of tension and stiffness in the back of the neck with restriction in movement. This may also give rise to the sensation that the head feels too heavy for the shoulders. Pain may spread down between the shoulder blades, across the shoulders and down the arms to the hands which in turn may also feel weak and heavy. It is felt that this is due to reflex inhibition of the muscles by pain in the arms thereby giving the sensation of extra power being required to overcome the pain reflex. The pain may be accompanied by numbness or tingling, involving the ring and fifth fingers. The cause of the tingling is not clearly defined. In some cases it may follow the dermatome from the appropriate cervical nerve root. It has been suggested that if there is an element of rotation in the neck at the time of the accident, for instance leaning forward and turning to the right or the left, then there is more likely to be damage to the facetal joints. Other suggestions of the pain have been that it is caused by compression of the nerve roots as they pass between some of the muscles of the neck and the collarbone.

On occasion claimants will complain of anterior neck pain in the area of the throat. Sometimes this is associated with difficulties in swallowing. This may be due to some bruising in the area of the soft tissues surrounding the anterior longitudinal ligament and causing compression of the oesophagus. Generally difficulty in swallowing indicates a more severe injury. Very occasionally, possibly due to bruising and swelling around the laryngeal nerves, hoarseness has been reported but this is usually short-lived.

Tinitus

Some people complain of ringing in the ears (*tinitus*). In the initial phase this may simply be due to the noise of the incident but it can persist and appears to be due to either disturbance of the vestibular apparatus in the ears or by damage to the nerves such as a sympathetic chain, part of which radiates into the neck which might theoretically be damaged. This may also go some way to explaining the possibility of vertigo or dizziness. Unfortunately, especially in the elderly, these symptoms may persist in the long-term.

Psychological

Finally, there may be psychological symptoms. Commonly there is some short-term resistance about getting into a car either as a passenger or a driver but not infrequently there is also a complaint of being hyper-vigilant. This often, but not always, mirrors the nature of the accident for instance being stopped and seeing a vehicle approach from behind; or driving along and seeing cars approach quickly from a side junction. In the initial phases there may be difficulty sleeping which may be due to pain but also to a tendency to have flashbacks of the incident. Very occasionally this could result in nightmares. It is unusual for flashbacks to occur when undertaking normal activities, and when is present for a prolonged period it is suggestive of a more severe anxiety disorder such as Post Traumatic Stress Disorder (Chapter 7).

THE INFLUENCE OF PRE-EXISTING PATHOLOGY

Pre-existing problems in the cervical spine are not uncommon and may compound the injury and the claimant's reaction to it. One in two hundred of the population experiences spontaneous onset cervical pain which is not attributable to any obvious factor. Degenerative changes in the neck appear with increasing frequency over the age of forty, and given the incidence of road traffic accidents, many people have been involved in more than one collision and may have ongoing symptomatology.

The history of a previous whiplash injury may give some pointers to the prognosis in the subject incident. Even if there have been a number of incidents, if these have cleared quickly and the claimant has been pain free for three to four years, then the previous history can be disregarded. However, if previous recovery was prolonged and if there were still symptoms immediately prior to the subject incident then there has clearly been an exacerbation of a pre-existing complaint and the prognosis becomes rather difficult to accurately assess. Under normal circumstances the acute phase will settle down over six to nine months towards the *status quo ante*, however symptoms may remain at a slightly greater level than they were immediately prior to the present incident.

As part of the ageing process, degenerative changes in the neck may render the cervical spine rather less mobile and more vulnerable after any trauma. Degenerative changes increase with age and over 50% of those over the age of fifty have changes visible on x-ray or MRI scanning. In these cases the recovery may be somewhat prolonged with at least some residual symptoms persisting into the long-term. It is important however to note that in those with degenerative changes, under normal circumstances there will be restriction in neck movements anyway, even if the claimant was not aware of them prior to the accident. Therefore, although the claimant may complain of restriction following the incident, the apparent lack of movement may well be within the normal range for the age group or the underlying condition of the spine.

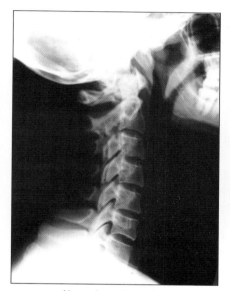 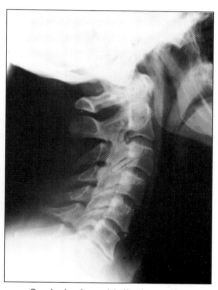

Normal cervical spine

Cervical spine with lipping and narrowing of the C6/7 disc space

Fig. 8 Osteophytic lipping

Initially the changes are commonest at the level of C5 to C7. There may be bony reaction giving calcification known as *osteophytic lipping* on x-ray (see figure 8). The disc spaces may be narrowed as the discs bulge posteriorly. This narrowing also results in more pressure being placed on the interfacetal joints thereby increasing the stress at that level and the general wear and tear. This causes osteophyte formation in these joints, stenosis of the foramena through which the nerves pass or joint sclerosis at the interfacetal level. The net result is trapping of the nerves giving pain and paraesthesia or pins and needles going across the shoulders and into the arms. Other symptoms may include a feeling that the head is too heavy for the shoulder or sharp pain on turning the head quickly.

PROGNOSTIC INDICATORS

In those who do not recover quickly, some particular characteristics may be noted. Patients over the age of sixty tend to recover more slowly. Initially it would appear that males recover more quickly that females but this effect disappears after the first year. A previous history of neck pain and radiological degenerative changes are associated with a longer duration of significant pain as are previous injuries which were still giving rise to symptoms at the time of the present incident. Pain which radiates for any length of time into the occipital region, down the arms or into the back between the shoulder blades have a worse prognosis. There is also a poor prognosis if there are any objective signs such as muscle spasm, loss of the normal curvature and if there is a decreased range of motion at one level, for instance between C5 and C6, particularly when pain in the neck is increased by coughing.

It would also appear that those injured in rear end shunts in general have a worse outlook than those involved in impacts from other directions. There would also seem to be a tendency for a greater degree of injury in front seat passengers when compared to drivers possibly due to the ability of the drivers to brace themselves against the steering wheel.

If symptoms are prolonged, then decreased use of the neck muscles may lead to some real weakness in the area especially if it is compounded by the prolonged use of a collar. It is therefore particularly important to start exercise at an early phase and to get back to normal activities including work. Further, any cervical collar should be discarded at the earliest available opportunity.

Finally, physical symptoms may be prolonged in those with a poor psychological profile. It could of course be stated that those who are capable of getting back to work at an early phase are less seriously injured but long-term studies have shown that this is not necessarily the case. Undoubtedly the psychological make-up and the subsequent reaction of the claimant to the incident does have considerable effect on the level and longevity of symptoms.

PHYSICAL EXAMINATION

Examination should begin immediately the claimant enters the room noting their ease of movement and how they sit. It should be noted whether or not they turn their head easily during conversation, whether they turn their whole body to face the examiner and the ease with which they can move their neck from side to side. Also, normal movements during conversation should be observed such as nodding or shaking the head. It is most unusual to be so completely rigid that the head cannot move at all. They should be observed taking off and putting on clothing, for instance a jacket, coat or pullover to see whether the movements correspond to the later movements noted on formal testing. Finally, observation should be continued after the formal examination until the claimant leaves the room. A parting comment when the patient reaches the door can elicit an unguarded and natural movement of the head.

On formal testing, the resting position of the head and the trunk should be noted particularly as regards the level of the shoulders. It is extremely unusual for muscle spasm to cause elevation of the shoulders but there may be loss of the normal curvature in the back of the neck. Examination should proceed in order, going straight down from the base of the skull to the area between the shoulders then along the muscles of the sides of the neck including the sternocleidomastoid muscles and out across the trapezius muscles to the shoulders. There may be particular areas of tenderness at the base of the skull and over the prominence of the seventh cervical vertebra. Note should be taken as to whether there is tenderness on palpation of the muscles themselves down the sides of the neck, across the shoulders and into the area between the shoulder blades. It is not uncommon, especially in the early phases to find some specifically painful spots particularly in the muscles at the base of the neck on either side, so called trigger spots which may also be noted down the sides of the vertebrae, possibly related to the facetal joints. There may be spasm in the musculature. This may involve the trapezius but of particular note is the erector scapular muscles on either side feeling like a tight band radiating from the sides of the cervical spine down to the upper inner aspect of both scapulae. These fibres are very distinct and easily palpated when they are in spasm. On occasion, a claimant will complain of tenderness on the lightest touch along the neck and shoulders and this may be an indication of a functional overlay. Similarly, a complaint of increased neck pain on axial loading by putting pressure on the top of the head with the hand would be difficult to explain on a physical basis.

Movements should be checked in all modalities, remembering the normal ranges and their variation with age. The movements to be elicited are flexion and extension, rotation to either side and lateral flexion to either side. Movements of both shoulders should then be tested including abduction, flexion and extension, internal and external rotation. Abduction should be continued above shoulder height with observation in the movement of the shoulder blades. This movement may cause an increase in pain going across the top of the shoulders and into the sides of the neck.

Examination of the upper limbs is both sensory and motor. The relative strengths of flexion and extension of the elbow and wrist should be noted along with the power of supination and pronation at the wrist as well as the handgrip. Any areas of abnormal sensation should be mapped by the claimant and carefully recorded. This may be of value in future when the examination is reproduced. Finally, there should be a check of the main reflexes in the upper limbs.

Any claimant who complains of symptoms in the neck associated with a decreased range of movement possibly weeks after the incident will require at least x-rays of their cervical spine which may show underlying abnormalities up to and including small fractures.

The examination and the x-ray findings then allow classification by the Quebec System.

QUEBEC SYSTEM

Grade	Characteristics	Prognosis
0	No complaints and no signs.	N/A
1	Complaints of neck pain and stiffness with tenderness but no signs.	Patients usually clear within 6 months and apart from painkillers require no specific therapy.
2	Complaints of neck pain and stiffness with tenderness and some musculo-skeletal signs such as point tenderness and limitation of movement.	Patients require further methods of diagnosis and treatment including x-rays, physiotherapy and have a rather more guarded prognosis.
3	Severe neck pain and stiffness with rigidity of movement and neurological signs such as decreased tendon reflexes, muscle weakness and sensory loss.	As Grade 2.
4	As with Grade 3, associated with a fracture or a dislocation.	Patients will require immediate management which may include surgical intervention. Any consequent neurological damage may result in permanent disability.

CHAPTER HIGHLIGHTS

1 Whiplash injuries are associated with a variety of symptoms which may develop either immediately or gradually over the first week.

2 Most accident victims recover from whiplash effects within 6 months although in around 10% physical problems may persist in the long-term.

3 Prognosis is influenced by pre-existing pathology, including degenerative changes or the effects of previous injury as well as the characteristics and severity of the initial presentation.

5

Radiological Investigations

INTRODUCTION

In the majority of cases where there is a quick recovery, a detailed history and examination would be sufficient to allow for a reasoned discussion of the nature of the injuries and the likelihood of any subsequent problems. For those who do not recover quickly and who are left with continuing pain and stiffness, particularly if this radiates into the arms or down the back, plain radiographs may be helpful. It is important not to create the potential for further harm to patients by subjecting them to unnecessary radiation, so examiners should try to obtain sight of any contemporary x-rays which are available. It is entirely inappropriate to obtain x-rays for medico-legal purposes in someone who is pregnant. Computerised Tomography (CT) scans deliver a high dose of radiation and should not be organised unless there are very specific reasons to do so.

When x-rays are required for medico-legal purposes, it is important that they are reported by a radiologist who is skilled in giving such opinions. Routine reporting of x-rays in a hospital environment may not fully cover the subtleties that are required, such as any loss of the normal curvature of the spine or the presence of degenerative change. A typical simple report stating 'no acute bony injury' is far from sufficient in a medico-legal situation.

PLAIN X-RAYS OF THE CERVICAL SPINE

X-ray films are obtained by passing radiation through tissue onto an x-ray plate. These rays are blocked by bone and to a lesser degree by fat or muscle. They therefore are excellent for studying bony injury, alignment and the range of motion as well as any congenital abnormalities such as fusion of two vertebrae which may render the neck less mobile. They are not particularly good at showing damage to soft tissues such as cartilage or ligaments unless these have become calcified. They can however indicate an increased space in front of the vertebrae, for instance between the vertebrae and the air in the

43

oesophagus, which would be an indication of soft tissue swelling in the area. This may happen in acute injuries even if there has not been a fracture. The objective therefore is to see if there is any bony injury or underlying abnormality causing symptoms which may have been precipitated or exacerbated by the injury. Occasionally it is appropriate to obtain follow-up x-rays which may show progression of changes.

Three standard views are normally taken, these are: the lateral view, both flexion and extension, and a peg view.

The Lateral View

This should include views in flexion and extension to show normal movements of the neck and to exclude any suggestion of instability. To be acceptable, x-rays must show all seven vertebrae and the junction between C7 and T1. A loss of the normal curvature or lordosis of the spine is in keeping with muscle discomfort. The flexion and extension views may show a lack of normal movement or some evidence of instability consistent with damage to the ligaments. A decreased range of movement is particularly significant if such movement is restricted at one level only, this suggesting damage in that area. Caution has to be exercised with findings of instability. Some people have lax ligaments and a slight forward slip is not particularly significant. This is not an uncommon feature in childhood. It may also develop in diseases such as rheumatoid arthritis although in the vast majority of these cases there is a clear past history of problems in the neck.

Ligamentous damage may also be inferred when calcification appears in the ligaments, particularly the anterior longitudinal ligament although this can also be an incidental finding. X-rays taken in the early phase may show some widening of the soft tissue space between the cervical spine and the oesophagus suggesting oedema in the area or there may be a small underlying fracture of the vertebral body. Other fractures may be noted in the arch or perhaps an avulsion fracture which is basically a ligamentous injury of the posterior spinous process. Care needs to be taken since occasionally an abnormal ossification centre (a developmental lesion), may be present particularly in the spinous process and appear to be a separate piece of bone although it is well circumscribed, corticated and is not related to any injury.

Another fracture that may be present is a crush fracture, particularly of the anterior body of the vertebra. This is particularly significant if the loss of vertebral height is more than 15% because it leads to an increased likelihood of degenerative changes developing in the disc spaces above and below due to the abnormal angulation caused to the cervical spine.

X-rays may also reveal congenital abnormalities, such as fusion between the bodies of two vertebrae especially around the level of C5/6. There is no intervertebral disc at this level with the result that the spine is rather more rigid. More movement will therefore occur in the disc spaces immediately above and below the lesion and this has been noted to give rise to increased symptoms after neck trauma. Degenerative changes may be a feature with osteophyte formation and/or disc space narrowing. These are particularly noted at the C5/6 level although may occur anywhere throughout the neck. They appear with increasing frequency after the age of forty, but do not necessarily give rise to symptoms.

Finally, there may be changes associated with other disease processes such as the progressive inflammation and fusion of the cervical spine associated with conditions such as ankylosing spondylitis. Other diseases that can cause problems in the neck are rheumatoid arthritis, psoriasis and on occasion the secondary spread of cancer can cause bone destruction.

Plain x-rays may show other abnormalities such as extra ribs (the cervical rib). These are important since the nerve roots exiting the neck may be bent over the abnormal tissue, causing tingling and paraesthesia down the arms to the hand. Symptoms may develop for the first time following a whiplash injury possibly due initially to muscle spasm and then sagging of the shoulders.

Other Views

When the pain is high in the neck, a specific open mouth x-ray of the C1/C2 complex may show a fracture or instability of the odontoid peg. As these can be difficult to interpret these films should be reported by an expert radiologist skilled in the medico-legal process. Occasionally oblique views may be take to show the status of the facetal joints in terms of fusion or degenerative change.

Changes on x-ray do not necessarily correspond to levels of symptomatology. Calcification in ligaments and other degenerative changes may have been present for years without any symptoms and yet others, in whom the x-ray looks totally within normal limits, may have degenerative disc disease with protrusion into the spinal canal or into the area where the nerve roots pass through the intervertebral foramen.

COMPUTERISED TOMOGRAPHY (CT) AND MAGNETIC RESONANCE IMAGING (MRI) SCANS

CT and MRI scans are much better at showing the soft tissues as well as any incidental lesions in the spinal cord.

In order to obtain a CT scan, the patient is placed between the source of radiation and the sensor which rotates. This results in a digital display of computerised slices through a particular area which gives a much clearer image of the bony structure but is not particularly good for soft tissues. Multiple doses of radiation are required with potentially harmful effects especially if repeated.

The MRI is a passive scan, acting as a pure sensor of changes in the bodies own magnetic properties, induced when the tissues are subjected to a large magnetic field. This does not result in any radiation being transmitted to the tissues. It is in fact imaging the hydrogen nucleus which is particularly abundant in water and fat.

The MRI scan is much superior in showing soft tissues such as ligaments, discs and nerve tissue. While plain x-rays may look normal, the MRI scan can demonstrate degenerative changes in discs or even posterior bulging into the cord or its nerve roots. The MRI scan may therefore reveal problems directly related to the trauma or incidental lesions. An example of the latter would be a patient presenting with tingling in the arms and hands following a road traffic accident. X-rays may reveal no abnormality but an MRI scan could reveal a lesion in the cervical cord such as multiple sclerosis. This would account for the symptoms but is clearly unrelated to the accident.

There are a number of contraindications to MRI scanning and these should be explored with patients in advance. The main contraindication is the presence of any metal in tissues as this may be moved by the magnetic impulses and could cause serious complications. Examples include anyone who has had brain surgery since metal clips may have been used to secure blood vessels and may be dislodged by the magnetic field. Others may have small metallic fragments from shrapnel in the tissues of the neck or on occasions small flecks in the eye, due to occupational injuries. MRI scanning may also interfere with the working of cardiac pacemakers or artificial heart valves with metal components. Another drawback with the use of either MRI or CT scans is the fact that older scanning equipment was built like a tunnel and may not be tolerated by patients with claustrophobia or high levels of anxiety.

In conclusion, these newer forms of visualisation of the cervical spine may show lesions not apparent on ordinary x-rays and provide some objective findings to support a claimant's contention of continuing symptomatology. They therefore have an important role in medico-legal practice, but should not be used as a first line investigation.

OTHER INVESTIGATIONS

Occasionally in claimants with prolonged symptoms in the arms and particularly the hands it may be appropriate to carry out nerve conduction studies. Carpal tunnel syndrome has been reported as an associated complication of a whiplash injury to the neck, possibly due to swelling around the wrist or direct trauma to the wrist in the impact, for instance a driver holding the wheel. Nerve conduction studies can determine if there is any problem with the nerves to the hand and at what level that problem arises, either at the wrist giving a true carpal tunnel syndrome or higher up in the neck where the nerves go through the scalene muscles causing a thoracic outlet syndrome.

CHAPTER HIGHLIGHTS

1 Radiological investigations are not necessary in those who make a quick recovery.

2 Where pain and stiffness is persistent, contemporary x-rays should be considered in the first instance before requesting investigations for medico-legal purposes.

3 These should always be reported by an experienced radiologist skilled in interpreting and reporting findings for legal situations.

4 When their use is justified by protracted symptomatology, CT and MRI scans may show lesions not apparent on plain x-rays and can be useful analytical and prognostic techniques. Contraindications to both should be full explored with claimants.

Clinical Course and Management of Whiplash Injury

INTRODUCTION

The majority of whiplash injuries are minor and cause no more than short-term discomfort. In more protracted cases the greatest improvement occurs over the first six months. There continues to be a rapid decline in the proportion of patients complaining of symptoms over the following six to nine months with the recovery rate slowing after that. Severe ligamentous damage can be quite slow to heal, and indeed more than 10% go on to suffer long-term disability. However, there still may be spontaneous improvement even after five to eight years. Therefore, in patients who continue to have a lot of pain after the first three to six months, it is not really feasible to give a good idea of prognosis until after 18 months to two years have elapsed.

The normal sequence of recovery will be influenced by any underlying pathology in the cervical spine and by the effects of treatment.

COMMON METHODS OF TREATMENT

Most whiplash patients will be treated by their GP and the following treatments are fairly standard.

In the initial 24 to 48 hours, pain may be eased by the intermittent application of ice packs and the use of anti-inflammatory drugs, one of the most common being Ibuprofen. These combined with gentle exercise tend to keep down the swelling in the muscle fibres leading to decreased stiffness. Stiff cervical collars are no longer prescribed as early exercise has been shown to hasten the recovery. However, a soft collar may be useful on an intermittent basis for a couple of weeks to relieve discomfort. Support for the neck is also useful in bed. High pillows should be avoided and a rolled up towel placed behind the neck may help to keep the normal curvature and relax the muscles. Occasionally, sedative drugs are prescribed to help relieve muscle spasm. In the long-term, their use may be counter-productive, causing initial sleepiness and then difficulty in sleeping when attempts are made to withdraw them. This becomes a vicious circle and the patient may end up using sleeping tablets.

It is probably inappropriate to apply heat to the neck within the first 48 to 72 hours as this may encourage vasodilatation and excess bleeding can lead to swelling and therefore increased stiffness. After that time, the application of local heat, for instance with an anti-inflammatory rub, warming the towel around the neck before using it at night or other local treatments for the muscles such as the use of interferential therapy by physiotherapists, may be of benefit. The early commencement of exercises to promote neck mobilisation has been shown to be effective when it is used to the limits of reasonable tolerance. More active physiotherapy treatments may be useful in those patients whose symptoms do not settle after the first few weeks. On the other hand, the use of traction has not been shown to be of benefit and indeed in some patients may actually make matters worse.

In those patients who have very specific trigger points of locally defined areas of muscle tenderness, infiltration with local anaesthetic may produce some relief and claims are also made for the use of acupuncture for the relief of spasm. Other modes of management such as the use of aromatherapy may help by tending to relieve anxiety and strain, thus leading to relaxation of the muscle tissue in some cases.

SURGERY

Some very severe injuries with bony and ligamentous damage may require surgical stabilisation. However, in the majority of cases, surgery has no place unless very specific lesions are noted. These may include encroachment of the cervical spine or nerve roots by a posterior protruding disc or narrowing of the root canal in the intervertebral foramen. Local corticosteroid injection into the facetal joints or around the local area may be helpful in both diagnosis and also be of prognostic value with regards to whether or not surgery may be useful. Local anaesthetic infiltration may give some pain relief but it is usually short-lived.

PRE-EXISTING PATHOLOGY

Degenerative changes in the neck undoubtedly tend to be associated with a poor prognosis but of themselves are of little predictive value. Degenerative change includes osteophyte formation, calcification and protrusion of the discs as well as calcification of the ligaments. These features do represent an area of increased vulnerability basically because the neck is not as supple as would otherwise have been the case. Also, degenerative changes are more prevalent in older people and they may well have a poorer prognosis merely because of their age.

It is important to note that in a number of studies no significant progression of degenerative change in the neck was noted over a number of years after an accident other than that which would have normally been expected. It is not known therefore whether increased age and evidence of pre-existing degenerative change are independent prognostic factors.

LATE ONSET OF SYMPTOMS

Further symptoms rarely develop after the initial few months and the tendency is to reach a static phase. Once this has been established, any increasing severity or the development of new symptoms is unlikely to be due to the accident in question but rather to other factors such as the natural progression of the underlying disease process. Therefore, symptoms developing five to six months after the accident are most unlikely to be related to it in any way. The only real exception is when there has been a fracture leading to abnormalities of vertebral structure, particularly alignment, which may perhaps provoke a long-term increase in degenerative change.

RETURNING TO WORK AND NORMAL ACTIVITY

The timing of a return to work depends on many features including the level of symptoms, the nature of the work and the psyche of the individual concerned. It is also influenced heavily by age. Work involving heavy physical activities such as lifting may exacerbate pains in the neck and shoulders. Pain may also be exacerbated in claimants whose job requires them to sit for a prolonged length of time in one position, for instance writing at a desk or using a computer. Driving a car or heavy vehicle, particularly if it does not have power steering may also increase symptoms. Similarly there would be an effect on hobbies and sporting activities which can lead to loss of amenity.

Undoubtedly, any lengthy interruption to an individual's normal work, hobby or sporting activities may decrease the likelihood of establishing normal activity in the long-term. Indeed some people have lost their job because they are unable to perform their work properly for several months. Some may lose interest in a hobby or feel they have become too old to go back to sport after a lay-off of several months. Their lifestyle may therefore be markedly altered as a direct consequence of the accident and they continue to experience a sense of loss.

CHAPTER HIGHLIGHTS

1 Most whiplash injuries demonstrate significant recovery in the initial six months.

2 For those with persistent symptoms prognosis is better left to 18-24 months post accident.

3 Pre-existing degenerative changes are not normally exacerbated by whiplash but symptoms may be.

4 It is most unusual for new symptoms to develop after six months.

5 The timing of return to work is dependent on a number of factors including nature of occupation, motivation and particularly age.

7

Psychological Aspects of Whiplash Injury

INTRODUCTION

In most medico-legal reports, the major emphasis is placed on the physical outcomes for the patient following a trauma. Often less attention is paid to the emotional aspects of the accident which are common and can have a considerable effect on the ability to cope with everyday life in the longer term. The emotional and psychological impact of a road traffic accident may be compounded by social factors such as isolation, financial worries or family pressures. An example would be the impact of job loss on a lone parent or in a family where there is no other source of income.

At one end of the scale there may be very little psychological impact with perhaps only a short-lived upset and possibly some reactive anger around the time of the incident. However, at the other end of the scale, for some victims the psychological aspects may take precedence. In at least 30% of cases there is some form of residual psychological problem after one year. Whilst not normally intrusive into every day activities, for some people there can be disabling and pathological emotions. These may manifest as an overreaction to residual physical symptoms giving a level of disability which is disproportionate to the actual injury. The psychiatric response may also exacerbate some pre-existing conditions such as myelo-encephalopathy (ME) and irritable bowel syndrome (IBS) as well as skin conditions such as eczema or psoriasis. In some cases these may be provoked by the trauma and may appear for the first time in the weeks following the accident. This combination of physical and psychological trauma may also be responsible for exacerbations of underlying disorders in the central nervous system and spinal cord such as multiple sclerosis (MS).

Finally, any psychological over reaction to physical pain may prolong the loss of use of muscles for instance in the neck and the arm, causing consequent loss of muscle bulk. This leads to further weakness giving a somatic reality to the psychological perceptions and thus forming a cycle which may be difficult to break. Therefore, it is important after any trauma to take account of the interaction between the physical and psychological effects of the trauma and the personality and circumstances of the individual concerned.

AETIOLOGY OF PSYCHOLOGICAL COMPLICATIONS

Head Injury

There may be direct trauma to the head as a result of contact with a hard object such as the headrest, the door or the roof. The consequence may be unconsciousness for several minutes due to direct brain injury or perhaps a concussion causing the claimant to be dazed with or without some short-term memory loss, some dizziness or nausea. Headaches may persist over the longer term. Such trauma can lead to the loss of the normal function of the brain and may be compounded by various medications such as high doses of painkillers and other treatments given to relax muscles. These sedatives can also cause tiredness and depression in susceptible individuals.

Other Physical Injury

The second factor that can have an effect on the psychological outcome relates to the nature and extent of physical injuries suffered. Pain and stiffness may cause limitation in all aspects of life such as work, leisure pursuits and relationships both within the family and of a social nature. There is also the potential for job loss, reduced promotion prospects or loss of status with consequent financial implications.

Psychological Trauma

There may also be direct psychological trauma. Indeed, this can occur without any physical injuries at all. For instance, being afraid for one's life as a consequence of being trapped in wreckage for any length of time or simply being exposed to serious injuries and other horrific sights at the scene of an accident, can be very disturbing and for some may have long-term psychological consequences. There may be a feeling of guilt in the 'lucky survivor' if others involved in the accident were fatally injured. These inward effects may have outward manifestations such as anger towards those who have been deemed responsible for the accident. This anger develops as part of a loss reaction, not necessarily just to the loss to life, limb or amenity, but also more general upset at the damage to the motor vehicle or simply a reaction to the loss of freedom to get around. When such loss is severe such as in situations where there are ongoing physical injuries or perhaps the death of a loved-one, anger is a natural part of the bereavement cycle and is necessary before any resolution can occur. When anger is disproportionate to the event or when it is pervasive, it can interfere with an individual's psychological recovery.

WHO IS MOST AT RISK?

A lot of the psychological complications of the accident originate from the perceptions of the individual. How someone perceives an incident depends on their psychological make-up which is coloured by previous experience. Some will have been well-balanced and well-adjusted psychologically prior to the incident. Others may have had a tendency to react to stress with anxiety or aggression. Some may have shown some previous psychiatric traits, such as prolonged neurosis or depression and may have had previous medical interventions. This underlying state can be exacerbated by the stress of the accident. Others who are potentially at greater risk include those who live in adverse social circumstances without adequate support from family and friends and in tenuous financial circumstances, perhaps compounded by the accident.

It has been shown that symptoms are generally more protracted in those who are particularly distressed around the time of the accident or in the early post-accident period. For someone who is trapped in the car, the fear of a life threatening consequence may persist even when extracted from the vehicle, especially if they are immobilised by various straps and headrestraints and transported by a siren-blaring ambulance. In addition, they may be fully aware of the various medical interventions taking place in the Accident and Emergency department and this can be a very frightening experience if they see concern in the individuals tending to them and if they do not receive adequate explanation and reassurance throughout the process.

Recovery may be protracted because of persistent physical problems or if they have ongoing reminders of the incident. The medico-legal process may itself contribute to this, especially if there is an element of confrontation such as a dispute over who is responsible for the accident, leading to distress and anger and possible frustration if the process is delayed.

Over the last decade there has been a fad for debriefing after accidents, but this has been shown to be counter-productive and is no longer recommended. Unfortunately, the nature of the medico-legal process, with constant reminders of the incident is likely to have a similar effect and the more quickly such issues can be dealt with, the better.

TYPES OF DISORDER

There are five main recognised types of disorder:

Concussive Disorder

This basically refers to the functioning of the brain which may be impaired following concussion. Symptoms such as headache, inability to concentrate and some impairment of short-term memory may be in evidence. These problems may be compounded by medication.

Adjustment Disorder

This can be a mix of anxiety and depression and is seen as a reactive response to the incident and to any physical symptoms produced. There may be a pre-existing propensity to develop such symptoms which include a depressed mood, anxiety and worry, and feelings of an inability to cope, to plan or continue in the present situation. These features interfere markedly with the daily routine. Particularly in teenagers, adjustment disorders can be demonstrated as aggression. In younger children symptoms may include bedwetting, thumb-sucking or problems with speech development; in other words, interference with the normal coping mechanisms and a decrease in social functioning. Symptoms increase when one is tired, for instance having difficulty in sleeping or, in the elderly, perhaps because of organic factors. The onset of an adjustment disorder is fairly immediate but being reactive it should start to ease within a month and clear within six months or so of the incident, or slightly longer if there are any significant physical symptoms. If it is more prolonged it merges with other chronic disorders.

Anxiety Disorder

Anxiety disorders are based on a feeling of lack of safety. They are evoked by memories of certain well-defined situations, generally external to the individual and which are not currently dangerous. There is therefore a situation-avoidance or certain situations that are endured with a feeling of dread. Feelings may be provoked by contemplation of something occurring and are associated with a pre-existing tendency to depression especially in the female. It may therefore manifest as fear, for instance a fear of travel, particularly as a passenger where there is a lack of direct control, or a fear of the particular location where the accident occurred or a similar location or set of circumstances. An example would be experiencing acute anxiety while sitting in a parked car and seeing another vehicle come close behind, or driving along a road and observing a vehicle approaching from a side road. It is basically a high level of arousal caused by being hyper-alert to the situation. In more extreme phases it can lead to panic attacks and these usually occur outside the home, for instance in crowds, such as whilst shopping or on a bus. Panic can also manifest when travelling alone and the feeling is one of an overwhelming need to immediately escape from the situation often to the safety of home. It is not delusional; the victim is usually perfectly aware of what is happening.

Anxiety disorders give rise to intrusive thoughts day and night and if particularly bad can become by definition Post Traumatic Stress Disorder (PTSD). This is a very delayed and protracted response and the likelihood of PTSD is increased if there is a previous psychiatric history. It usually begins within six months and the panic attacks are characterised by an adrenaline response of sweating, palpitations, feeling faint with chest pain and a feeling of dizziness or unreality. Other symptoms can include a dry mouth and the patient may also complain of tingling throughout the body. Once established, PTSD is very difficult to treat.

Depressive Reaction

These are characterised by an inability to function due to apathy and indecisiveness, a flat affect with feelings of tiredness, loss of energy, worthlessness and possibly inappropriate guilt; there is great difficulty in thinking or concentrating. When these continue they are usually of a constitutional background, that is, the claimant is prone to depression and this has either been finally initiated by or exacerbated by the stress of the accident.

Somatoform Disorder

Somatoform disorder implies that the psychological disturbance is causing or exacerbating the physical symptomatology. Presentation is of persistent, severe and distressing pain and the characteristics are such that the level of symptoms may not be explicable on a physical basis. Also, for no obvious reason, symptoms may markedly deteriorate over time leading to an increasing loss of function. Usually it is not diagnosed for at least two years after the incident and is characterised by refusal of the victim to accept the cause. It also inevitably results in an impairment of normal social and family functioning possibly combined with depression and anxiety.

This type of disorder is the most difficult to diagnose and is the most controversial since it obviously merges with the concepts of 'compensation neurosis' or 'malingering'. This dilemma is reinforced in cases where claimants are inclined to slightly exaggerate the level of symptoms, possibly due to anger or frustration when they feel they are not being adequately listened to or that the guilty party may 'get away with it'. Nevertheless somatoform disorders are a very real entity and may become obvious when stress flares up obvious skin conditions such as psoriasis or eczema. A flare-up of a feeling of pain is equally real.

Unfortunately, all of the disorders are not necessarily seen in isolation and may appear in various combinations making treatment complex, difficult and often protracted.

LOSS OF AMENITY

Work, leisure and relationships may all be affected by physical problems consequent on the accident and are just as effectively interfered with by psychological complications. The actual outcome is therefore the net result of the physical complications as modified or compounded by the psychological consequences. 'Stoic' individuals may get on with their lives in spite of considerable discomfort and may rightly feel aggrieved that just because they continue in their normal every day activities, their level of symptoms are not necessarily given the consideration they deserve. On the other hand, those with significant psychological problems may also be aggrieved that, although their physical symptoms may be of a lesser degree, the psychological effects are such that there is considerable and very real interference with their ability to cope. Consequently, the outcomes for individuals following trauma should not be described in purely statistical terms but should take a more holistic view based on a global assessment of the particular individual's physical and mental state in the context of their social environment.

EFFECTS OF TREATMENT

A number of studies have shown that of patients presenting at an early stage with psychological complications or who are extremely frightened when first seen by the GP or at an Accident and Emergency department, up to one third may have significant problems at the end of a year. In those who have persistent problems after five to six months, it has been shown that treatment by a Clinical Psychologist or Psychiatrist is of great benefit. Improving/enhancing the patient's underlying mood can decrease anxiety and even reduce physical manifestations such as pain or weakness. Physiotherapy from an early stage has also been shown to be of benefit, not just from the purely physical point of view but from a psychological aspect so long as the physiotherapist gives confidence and imbues a high expectation of recovery.

From a medico-legal point of view therefore, it is appropriate to look for a psychological assessment in those with any psychological manifestations lasting greater than six months.

CHAPTER HIGHLIGHTS

1 Although often neglected, the psychological consequences of whiplash injuries are common and often significant, particularly for those with other stresses in their social, economic or personal circumstances.

2 Psychological complications can be consequent of head injury, other severe physical injuries or be related to the emotional trauma experienced during or following an accident.

3 There are a number of clearly defined disorders including concussion, adjustment anxiety, depression and somatoform disorders. If not diagnosed and managed at an early stage these may become chronic with long-standing effects on the quality of life. This may be the case even in the absence of ongoing physical effects.

8

The Medico–legal Assessment and Report

INTRODUCTION

At the heart of medico-legal practice is the medico-legal assessment and report. Its function is to set out analytically which injuries were caused by the accident and the short and long-term effects of these injuries, physically and psychologically. In general, the short-term could be construed as the period up to the case being resolved and the long-term any period thereafter. The essence of the prognosis is an estimation on the balance of probabilities of the likelihood of continuance or deterioration of the condition in the longer term. This is the difference between what may happen: an outside chance but important if it is going to be a significant complication, what may possibly happen: which implies a greater likelihood of occurrence but still less than a 50% chance and what might probably happen: suggesting it is more likely than not to happen, that is, a 50% or greater chance.

What at first might seem a fairly straightforward process of determination based 'on the balance of probabilities' becomes more complicated in the presence of a pre-existing history of a similar problem, or a previous accident. Formal prognosis may also be made rather more difficult due to an inadequate history of the mechanism of the accident, for instance due to poor recollection by the claimant either of the accident itself or of their subsequent clinical course by the time they appeared for an examination.

Other factors which must be taken into account by the medical expert is the emotional and psychological status of individuals as well as the nature of their work and their particular lifestyle. Finally, account must be taken of any underlying physical abnormalities discovered during investigations. These may include underlying abnormalities in the structure of the spine such as osteo-arthritic changes which have not previously given rise to symptoms.

All of this therefore becomes the field of the medico-legal expert witness.

INITIAL INSTRUCTIONS

The initial letter of instruction from the solicitor to the medical expert should briefly address matters of fact surrounding the accident along with any specific areas which the solicitor wishes the expert to address. It is also helpful if the medical expert is aware at the outset whether or not there are pre-existing x-rays and if there is clearance for any further x-rays to be taken.

If there is any doubt, the medical expert should make direct contact with the instructing solicitor. This is essential, as it is surprising how often the claimant cannot remember seemingly obvious facts such as the date of the accident and its exact nature. If they were not the driver of the car some cannot remember exactly where they were sitting and whether or not they were wearing seatbelts. This is compounded if there is some amnesia as a result of the accident and therefore it is advisable that such information is included with the instructions. It is also valuable to have a list of the initial complaints as given to the solicitor since again it is not uncommon for claimants to forget to mention particular problems at the time of their examination especially if some of the problems cleared quickly and the report is not requested for many months after the incident. It is therefore recommended that a first report is obtained within a matter of months and subsequent reports, if required, a year or more later if there appear to be the likelihood of long-term consequences. There have been a number of attempts to formalise the structure of medico-legal reports, but many find this constrains individual style. Nevertheless, it is reasonable to point out some basic requirements under each heading.

THE FORMAT OF THE MEDICO-LEGAL REPORT

1 Preamble

2 Documentation

3 History

4 Injuries Sustained

5 Subsequent Management and Treatment

6 Past History

7 Present Complaints

8 On Examination

9 Comment and Prognosis

10 Statement of Independence

Preamble

The full name, age, sex and address of the claimant along with an occupational history should be provided. This would include the claimant's occupation at the time of the incident as well as at the date of the report since it may be necessary in the comment section to explain why there has been a change in occupation and the relevance to the subject incident. The date of the accident and the date of the report stating clearly whether this is a first report or a follow-up report should also included.

Documentation

This section should list any medical notes as well as records or any other documentary evidence, for instance an employer's work record supplied for the purposes of the report. It may also include a list of statements by the claimant or the police.

History

This section should start by stating the person from whom the history was obtained. It may be from the claimant, a relative such as a parent, or perhaps emanate from the solicitor's instructions. It is essential to ensure that this point is covered in case there is any dispute later on.

This should be followed by a concise history of the nature of the accident, such as is necessary to describe the forces involved. It should not attempt to apportion liability. It is important that this history is accurate since any discrepancy between the expert's report and the actual facts of the case lead to embarrassment during court proceedings. Medical experts should be careful with the language they use in reports. There is a completely different connotation put on a sentence if the expert states that the patient 'alleges' a fact to be true rather than the patient 'states' the fact. The use of the word 'allege' may be taken to imply that the expert does not quite believe the history given by the claimant.

The section should state whether or not the claimant was knocked out or dazed, how they got out of the vehicle, whether this was with or without assistance and whether they were capable of speaking to anyone at the time. It should mention whether any immediate first aid was rendered at the scene, by whom and where the claimant went afterwards, for instance to work, home or whether they were taken to hospital. The mode of travel is also significant, in particular whether or not they drove themselves home or to hospital or were taken by ambulance. Travelling in the back of an ambulance on a spinal board can be quite a nauseating experience and can give rise to headaches as well as being psychologically upsetting.

Sometimes a full history will not be available, for instance if the claimant was knocked out. If so, the history should include the last memory prior to the accident and the next memory following it in order to give an idea of the length of amnesia. It is important to note whether this is consistent with Accident and Emergency department records which may state for example 'fully alert on arrival'. It is not uncommon for a confused patient to appear to be fully alert when seen in an Accident and Emergency department, able to give some form of history, but still later forget a significant period of time; this is characteristic of a concussion injury.

Injuries Sustained

All injuries sustained in the accident should be listed along with any chronology involved and should include not just those injuries which were apparent immediately after the accident but also those which developed over the first week or 10 days. It is useful to have detailed within the solicitor's instructions the nature of injuries reported to him in case after a period of time some of the initial injures which healed fairly quickly may have been forgotten. Following this there should be a brief indication of the initial management and who administered treatment, for example, hospital staff or the GP, particularly since it may be necessary to obtain the appropriate notes. Management at this stage may include the treatment of wounds such as by glue, sutures or sticky tape, whether x-rays were taken including what the patient remembers being told about the results. Notes should be taken of any medications prescribed such as sedatives, painkillers or anti-inflammatory drugs and any discharge instructions such as to report to their GP, being given a referral for physiotherapy or having information provided on corrective exercise programmes.

It is important for the claimant to state what diagnosis was given to them at the time. Most Accident and Emergency departments are staffed by junior doctors, especially out of normal working hours, and their interpretation of x-rays is not always totally accurate. If there is any suggestion of a fracture then the medical expert should be alerted to the need to obtain the final discharge letter to the GP from the hospital or an official report on the x-rays from a radiologist. It is important to note that official x-ray reports may not be particularly complete and may omit to mention a loss of the normal curvature (lordosis) or degenerative changes in the neck, all of which may have a substantial impact on a long-term prognosis.

Finally, at this stage the claimant's initial reaction to the accident should be recorded. It is well known that those who are very distressed at the time they arrive in an Accident and Emergency department or to see their GP have a much higher likelihood of continuing psychological or even physical symptoms in the long-term.

Subsequent Management and Treatment

This section should document when treatment was commenced and whether it commenced immediately after the incident or was delayed by a number of days and if so, for what reason. It should also note the drugs prescribed and whether there was a referral for physiotherapy, when it commenced and for how long it lasted.

Each injury should be analysed in turn, giving an indication of:

1 How long the symptoms took to build up.
2 How long the symptoms were at their peak.
3 What has been the subsequent course.
4 Whether the claimant was off work. If so, when did the period off work commence, for how long and why.
5 Whether there just one period of absence from work or several either in blocks of time or individual days.
6 Whether there was any increase in symptoms when the claimant returned to work.
7 Did the claimant have to undertake lighter duties or need extra help for a period of time.
8 If the claimant is a housewife, what problems arose at home during normal housework duties such as vacuuming, making beds or looking after children.

At this stage there should also be some indication of other elements of interference with lifestyle such as having to give up sporting activities or hobbies and perhaps comment on relationships within the family or in a wider sphere such as the ability to go out and socialise.

Past History

A detailed account of any past history of problems with the neck or any other part of the back should be provided. A history of low back pain due to degenerative change may indicate the possibility of similar degenerative changes in the neck. Perhaps x-rays of the various areas have been taken in the past and could be available in GP notes and records which may subsequently be obtained.

It is vitally important to note whether there are any other illnesses which would have a bearing on the long-term outlook for the working life; for example the claimant may complain that he hurt his leg but already have problems with prolonged walking, perhaps due to angina or shortness of breath on exertion. A note should be made as to whether the claimant is right or left-handed since pains in one or other arm may obviously differentially affect the ability to work or undertake recreational activity. Even if there is no past history for which the claimant has been to see a doctor, they may give an indication that they were experiencing some intermittent aches and pains in their neck and back prior to the accident, for example getting out of bed or sitting at a computer at work.

Present Complaints

This may not always be included since most of the information is included in the earlier section on management. However, on occasions it is appropriate to list those complaints which are ongoing.

On Examination

The medical expert should be quite clear as to what constitutes either a subjective or an objective description of symptoms. The examination commences by observation of the claimant as soon as they enter the room and continues throughout the conversation and when they are putting on or taking off clothing. Movements noted at that time should be compared and contrasted with a formal examination of movement. It is important to note the claimant's posture, in particular with regard to the neck, whether the shoulders are raised or not and whether the head is held forward.

The examination is then continued, identifying what appears to be the active range of movement on examination of the neck, the shoulders, the arms and the back noting whether or not there are any restrictions. These should be recorded against an estimate of the normal range. Any tendency for specific movements to increase the level of symptoms should also be noted, along with any inconsistencies. In particular, the medical expert should list incongruous findings such as pain in the back of the neck on light axial loading by pushing on the top of the head, any tenderness on the lightest touch of the musculature or extreme reactions either locally or by movement when touched.

Any incongruity between movements demonstrated should be pointed out; for instance, if the claimant holds himself very stiffly and appears to have difficulty with movement of the shoulders and elbows such as would make it impossible to feed himself. On occasion, some claimants will appear to have difficulty bringing the arms above shoulder height and yet have a normal abduction of the shoulders to 90 degrees. Any movement above this level is from the whole shoulder girdle and not from the shoulder joint and therefore, whereas it may cause pain, it should not be an impossibility.

In the elderly there may be central cord lesions in the cervical area (see chapter 2). These may give rise to signs and symptoms in the lower limbs with lesser or no signs at all in the arms. Therefore, there should be a careful attention paid to the neurological status of the lower limbs which may indicate a lesion at the cervical cord level in a patient who has osteo-arthritic changes.

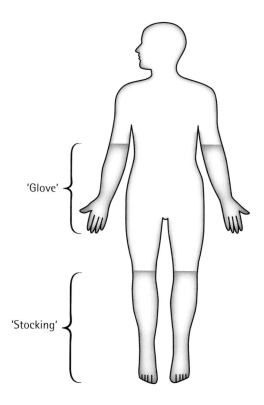

Fig. 9 Paraesthesia in a Glove and Stocking distribution showing areas of abnormal sensation

On examination of the arms the claimant should be asked to map out any loss of sensation or clearly delineate areas of paraesthesia, for instance on the fingers and the hand. Whilst it would not be correct to say all paraesthesia would conform to a nerve distribution or loss of sensation, paraesthesia in a glove or stocking distribution (see figure 9) would be extremely difficult to explain on a physical basis. It is important to note whether they appear to resist movements on examination which they otherwise demonstrate naturally when not being formally examined.

Finally, this section should indicate the claimant's reactions during the history-taking and examination. Some may be visibly upset and close to tears when thinking over the accident and it is important to note this level of distress. If this distress is still apparent more than five to six months after the accident then it would be an indication for a psychiatric referral.

Comment and Prognosis

This section should begin with a summary of the accident and the subsequent history. All symptoms should be discussed mentioning those which have cleared up and by what time. Relevant findings on examination should be reviewed and whether or not there is any likelihood of recurrence. If all the symptoms have disappeared then the prognosis section should be relatively straightforward.

A reasoned argument is expected by the Court as to the nature of the residual symptoms, the links with the accident and the likely subsequent course. This cannot be an exact science but should be a well-reasoned 'guestimate' as regards outcome. Residual symptoms or signs should be dealt with one at a time discussing whether or not they are compatible with the stated injury, with the physical findings and with any relevant past history or medical condition, perhaps gleaned from the notes, including the following points:

1 What is the likely diagnosis?
2 What is the influence of this diagnosis on ability now or in the future to work, in the home or outside of it, to leisure activities or the ordinary enjoyment of life with friends and relatives including children?
3 Is the condition likely to deteriorate with time and if so why giving a possible timescale?
4 If there have been pre-existing problems, for instance degenerative changes on x-ray, what is the likelihood that these would have become symptomatic and in what timescale?

5 In what way therefore has the accident altered the natural progression and is there liable to be any restriction in the ability to work until normal retirement age?

The medical expert must be aware of the legal aspects leading to the levels of award. This includes not only the pain and suffering at the time of the incident but also in the longer term. For example, are there likely to be any problems at work or with leisure or social activities including the loss of enjoyment of trips such as a holiday, for instance if the claimant would normally go skiing.

It may not be possible for the report to give an accurate prognosis at that time, either because of ongoing levels of symptoms or a requirement for further information. It may be necessary to obtain results of other tests including x-rays, scans or nerve conduction studies or to have sight of GP notes and records or occupational records looking both at the pre-accident history and the subsequent course. Any prognosis given under such circumstances should be guarded until other evidence is gathered.

Finally, the nature of some of the symptoms and signs may fall outside the direct expertise of the author of the report. If so, this should be clearly stated along with suggestions as to which other experts may be required, for instance a dental adviser or a psychiatrist.

Reports should therefore be methodical and clear, giving as much assistance as possible on the prognosis, with well-reasoned arguments supporting the opinion.

Statement of Independence

At the end of the report, courts in the UK require a statement by the medical expert to the effect that 'the contents of this report are true to the best of my knowledge and belief'. This reminds the expert that no matter whether instructed by the claimant or the defence, the role is to be of assistance to the Court by being as accurate, fair and objective as possible. The aim is to remain independent and unbiased and indeed when medical reports are shared, the expert has a duty to adopt a similar attitude when discussing any perceived discrepancy in another expert's report.

CHAPTER HIGHLIGHTS

1 The medico-legal assessment and report is crucial to the legal process in determining the appropriate level of compensation commensurate with injuries sustained and their consequence.

2 Reports should follow a standard format outlining the medical facts in chronological order, leading to a well-reasoned discussion of the likely prognosis.

3 Regardless of who instructs them the role of the expert witness is to assist the Court by providing an independent, fair and objective opinion.

9

Giving Evidence in Court

INTRODUCTION

To the medical expert, credibility is everything and nowhere is this tested more than when giving oral evidence in court. The key to a successful practice as an expert witness lies therefore in the power of communication. A clear and confident delivery is required both when relaying facts and opinion and when answering questions under cross-examination. This level of excellence can only be achieved through careful preparation and planning.

PREPARATION

At least one week before the court date, the written evidence from all medical reports and subsequent clarifications should be thoroughly reviewed. The notes themselves should be prepared with highlighters and/or tabs on appropriate pages, for ease of reference. Potential areas of contention should be particularly highlighted, perhaps in red, and clear strategy reasoning to explain why one particular point of view would be more logical than another. Consideration should also be given as to whether any other props would be required such as supporting papers, x-rays, text books or journal articles in order to support any leading contention. Four or five working days should be sufficient time to gather such information and to determine its usefulness. At this stage it may also be appropriate to hold conversations with the instructing solicitor and/or barrister in order to make them aware of any issues, particularly the strengths and weaknesses of any opposing views.

It is of fundamental importance, that the medical expert recognises the position is not one of advocacy of either side but rather a duty to assist the Court in reaching a reasonable conclusion, whereby the judge, on the balance of probabilities, can come to a statement of fact. The medical expert must stick to the matters of fact of which they are aware and logically present the reasoning as to why they have come to a particular conclusion.

It is in the nature of the adversarial process, that barristers and, unfortunately some experts, can tend to personalise and emotionalise the issues in order to try and defend a particular stance. This can lead to a tendency for confrontation and should be strenuously avoided by the medical expert . A judge's finding of 'fact', does not mean that the expert is wrong in the Court's opinion but rather that, on a particular occasion, the judge favoured an opposing point of view based on the evidence presented. The truth and the finding of fact in a court are therefore not necessarily the same thing. The best defence to becoming emotionally involved is to be absolutely professional, clear on all the facts and ensure the appropriate evidence is readily available to back up any opinion.

If there has been no opportunity for a pre-trial meeting with the instructing solicitor or barrister, it is important that witnesses meet at an agreed time prior to the commencement of the court hearing. If this is not possible, the barrister should be informed at an early stage so appropriate alternative arrangements for a briefing can be made, since it cannot be emphasised enough that pre-trial consultations are vital in the presentation of any case.

During the consultation, the medical expert should review all aspects of the evidence and discuss with the barrister how it is going to be presented. The expert should point out the contentious issues, why they are contentious and how they might be dealt with. They should indicate how far they are willing to go in support of a line of argument and in particular, point out areas where they are not prepared to agree a particular point of view, explaining the reasons for this. The expert should not allow himself to be pushed into making any statement or comment which cannot be supported by the evidence. Remember that the barrister is an advocate for a particular individual, the expert is an assistant to the Court and must always maintain professional independence and integrity.

GOING INTO COURT

The medical expert must respect the Court and the proceedings at all times. If possible, he should arrive prior to the judge and stand when the judge enters, returning the judge's bow in a dignified way. Pagers and mobile phones should be turned off and a proper silence maintained unless absolutely necessary for the purposes of the case, for instance a quick word with the barrister or solicitor. Courts are formal environments and dress should be appropriate, with business suits being the normal dress code. It is important to remember that first impressions do count and judges are very sensitive to what is happening in their court. The expert witness relies on being accepted as credible and should not do anything which may undermine that credibility in the eyes of the Court. Body language at all times should reflect confidence but not arrogance.

While waiting to be called to the witness box, the medical expert should listen carefully to the introductory statement from the barrister, and the evidence given by any subsequent witness. He should focus on the case and consider how the evidence as being presented reflects on his own evidence and whether there are any new facts emerging that could have a bearing and if so, how that evidence could be handled. He should take note of the surroundings and in particular where the witness box is and how best to access it. On arrival in the witness box, the expert may be asked to stand and either swear an oath or affirm to 'tell the truth, the whole truth and nothing but the truth'. He will be asked to give his name and qualifications and should sit when invited to do so by the judge. The form of address is 'My Lord' or 'My Lady' in the Crown Court and High Court, 'Your Honour' in a lower court. A 'thank you' is an often missed common courtesy. Surprisingly many experts do not see the importance of this little ritual. It is one of the first chances the judge has to evaluate the witness before him and first impressions do count.

The witness should sit facing the judge, and although looking at the barrister when being asked questions, court protocol requires witnesses to face the judge when giving answers. This breaking of eye contact with the barrister is an important technique, especially under cross-examination, as it avoids any tendency to confrontation and allows the witness to think clearly before responding. Speech should be distinct and at a measured pace, and as the judge is likely to take notes, care should be taken to determine the appropriate speed. Jargon should be avoided whenever possible and when necessary it should be carefully explained. Occasionally a diagram such as a simple line drawing or a demonstration, for instance of a particular movement, may be of assistance. However this should not be overly simplistic since most judges will have experience in dealing with similar cases.

When the expert wishes to read from a particular set of notes or other evidential materials, if not already directed to do so for instance by the barrister, it is a courtesy to ask permission of the judge: 'My Lord, if I may refer to my notes?'

When giving an opinion it is unwise to rely on the statement 'in my experience' unless directly asked. This can sound very patronising and it is much better to give third party evidence to back up any statements made. Speculative opinions which will not stand up to rigorous, intelligent cross-examination should be avoided and any opinion given should be kept balanced. It is important to accept and consider another point of view when proffered, assess whether it has merit and be prepared to compromise if necessary. Nothing destroys an expert's credibility more than holding fast to an opinion without clearly showing that they are taking other opinions fully into account and logically reasoning for or against a point of view.

Sometimes, during questioning, the expert may begin to realise that he is being led down a path that eventually leads to a conclusion with which he does not concur. Good barristers are skilled in such manipulation and it behoves the expert when he feels the questioning does not reflect his beliefs about a case to make this explicit to the judge along with the reasons why. This is particularly true when arguing from the particular to the general or vice versa for instance: 'Doctor, would you agree that the majority of such injuries to the neck recover in a relatively short space of time?' may lead to the conclusion: 'So in your opinion therefore this patient should have recovered in a maximum of three to four months?'. The barrister may not mention other factors such as previous injuries, the presence of degenerative change or the nature of employment which could have a bearing on the speed of recovery. The expert should draw this to the attention of the Court in order to keep a balanced view.

Just occasionally, entirely new evidence comes to light during cross-examination by the opposing barrister. If this happens an expert should never be rushed into making a judgement. It may be possible to give an immediate response; if not, the expert should ask for time to consider the new facts along with the previous evidence so that he can come to a reasoned conclusion. It would be very rare for a judge not to respond favourably to a reasonable request to consider an opinion in the light of new information, since indeed an opinion is only valid when seen in the context of the facts on which it was based. 'Doctor, would it surprise you to know ...', should register a warning that new information is going to be presented which may materially affect an expert's opinion and such information must be assimilated and reflected upon. If not, a rushed response may not stand up to scrutiny since the person asking the question will have had time to consider the impact of this particular piece of evidence and actually expects it to materially affect the outcome of the case.

Finally, the medical expert must have very clear boundaries around their area of expertise and strenuously avoid being challenged to give an opinion for which they are not qualified. A skilled barrister will expose such an indiscretion and may well exploit the situation in order to throw doubt on the validity on the rest of the evidence presented.

In conclusion therefore, the medical expert needs to carefully plan and prepare their evidence and demonstrate excellent communication skills and above all, self-discipline in the presentation of their opinions as oral evidence in court. They must understand that their opinion is given in context and is only valid as along as the context does not change. They must remain professional at all times and avoid becoming emotionally involved with the case, recognising that their reputation depends on being of assistance to the Court. Occasionally this may require a change of opinion rather than attempting to defend an indefensible position.

CHAPTER HIGHLIGHTS

1 An expert witness is not an advocate for a particular side but rather must regard himself as an officer of the Court.

2 Respect for court proceedings is essential. First impressions count and the expert should do nothing in regards to their dress or demeanour that may unintentionally undermine the credibility of the evidence.

3 Opinions are only valid when based on a specific context. Any opinion must stand up to rigorous and intelligent cross-examination. The expert should remain professional and unemotional and should be prepared to reconsider their opinion if the context is changed by the introduction of new evidence.

4 To be acknowledged as a credible medical expert and hence enjoy a successful career as an expert witness, it is imperative to gain the confidence of the Court in terms of respect for both the integrity of the individual and confidence in their opinion.

Index

acceleration injury 25
acute neck strain 13
adjustment disorder 56
age, effects of 14, 18, 20, 22, 36, 38-9, 45, 51
airbag 13, 31
anatomy of neck 15-24
annulus fibrosus 18
anxiety disorder 36, 56-7
arthritis 19-20
atlanto occipital joint 22
atlas 15, 17, 19
axis 17
brain injury 12, 34, 54, 56
calcification 37, 44-5, 50
car design 12
cerebro-spinal fluid 20
cervical,
    collar 38, 49
    rib 45
collision,
    force 12, 25-6
    rear end 11, 13, 25-8, 38
concussion 54, 56, 64
court,
    procedure 71-5
    report 68-9, 71
Crowe, Dr Harold 11
CT scan 30, 43, 46
degenerative change 14, 24, 30, 36-8, 43, 45-6, 50-1, 65, 68, 74
dens 17
depression 54-7
depressive reactions 57
dermatomes 19, 35
direction of impact 26-9, 31

disc,
    intervertebral 15, 16, 18, 37, 45
    protusion 19, 20, 37, 50
    structure 18, 24, 37
disorder,
    adjustment 56
    anxiety 36, 56-7
    concussive 56
    somatoform 57-8
dizziness 33-5, 54, 57
dura 16, 20
elevator scapula 21
emotional aspects 10, 53, 61
expert 9, 10, 61-9, 71-5
extension 12, 22-3, 27-9, 39-40, 44
facetal joints 17-18, 35, 37, 39, 45, 50
flashbacks 36
flexion 22-3, 27-8, 39-40, 44
fractures 11, 40, 44-5, 51, 64
fulcrum effect 12, 27
head injury 33-4, 54
headache 20, 34-5, 54, 56, 64
headrest 12, 26-7, 29, 31, 34, 54
impact,
    absorption 25
    direction of 26, 31
    force 12, 25-6
injury, acceleration 25
intervertebral,
    discs 15, 16, 18, 37, 45
    foramen 17, 19, 37, 45, 50
investigations, radiological 43-7
irritable bowel syndrome (IBS) 53
lateral flexion 22-3, 28-9, 39
ligamentous,
    calcification 44-5, 50

injury 11, 27, 30, 44, 49-50
ligaments 11, 15-16, 20, 27-8, 30, 44
ligamentum,
    flavum 20
    nuchae 16, 20
long-term problems 33, 36, 49, 54
lordosis 44, 64
loss of amenity 13, 51, 54, 58,
malingering 22, 58
manipulation 18
medical expert see expert
medico-legal report 9, 53, 61-9
MRI scan 14, 36, 46
multiple sclerosis (MS) 46, 53
muscle 20-1, 24-5, 27, 30, 35, 38-40,
    47, 49-50, 53-4
muscle spasm 21, 34, 38-9
myelo-encephalopathy (ME) 53
narrowing of foramina 19
neck movement,
    normal range 15, 22-3, 27-8, 37-9,
        44-5, 66
    on impact 11-12, 25-9, 31, 34
nerve conduction study 47, 69
nerves 11, 15-16, 19-21, 24, 30, 34-5,
    37, 46, 50
nucleus pulposus 18
odontoid peg 17, 45
oesophagus 16, 21, 30, 35, 44
osteo-arthritis 61, 67
osteophytic lipping 37
over breathing 34
pain,
    fibres 18
    relief 49-50, 54, 64
panic attacks 57
paraesthesia 34, 37, 45, 67-8
physical examination 38, 40, 66-8
post traumatic stress disorder (PTSD) 57
pre-existing pathology 13, 30-1, 36,
    50-1, 61, 68
pre-vertebral haematoma 30

prognosis 33
psychological aspects 9, 33, 36, 38, 53-9
Quebec System 40
radiation risk 43, 46
radiological investigations 43-7,
report writing 61-9
rheumatoid arthritis 44-5
rotation 11, 13, 22-3, 28-9, 35, 39
scalenus, anterior and medius 21
scan,
    CT 30, 43, 46
    MRI 14, 36, 46
seatbelt 12, 21, 25, 31, 62
semispinatus capitus 21
sheering force 12
soft tissue damage 11, 26, 30, 35, 43-4
somatoform disorder 57-8
sore throat 30, 35
speed, influence of 25-6
spinal,
    canal 15, 19-20, 45
    cord 15-16, 18, 20, 46, 67
    nerves 11, 15-16
sternocleidomastoid muscle 21, 39
surgery 50
swallowing 21, 30, 35
swelling 19, 21, 30, 35, 44, 47, 50
symptoms and signs 13, 24, 27, 33-40,
    51, 55-7
thoracic vertebra 13, 15, 19, 21, 27
trapezius muscle 21, 39
vision 34
treatment 49-50, 58, 65
vertebra 15-18, 43-5
vertebra prominens 17, 39
whiplash, definition 11, 13-14
x-ray 30, 36-7, 40, 43-6
x-ray, radiation risk 43, 46
zygopophyseal joint 18

Notes

Notes